Norris Bradbury
1909-1997

Norris Bradbury
1909-1997

Monograph 5

Virginia Nylander Ebinger, Editor

Los Alamos Historical Society
Los Alamos, New Mexico

Cover by Gloria Sharp.

Photographs courtesy of the Los Alamos Historical Society, the Los
Alamos National Laboratory, and the Bradbury family.

Edited by Virginia Nylander Ebinger

Library of Congress Cataloging-in-Publication Data

Bradbury, Norris, 1909-1997.
    Norris Bradbury, 1909-1997 / Virginia Ebinger, ed.--1st ed.
        p.cm. -- (The Los Alamos story ; monograph 5)
    Includes bibliographical references and index.
    ISBN 0-941232-34-4 (alk. paper)
    1. Physicists--United States--Biography. 2. Los Alamos
National Laboratory--History--20th century. 3. Atomic bomb--
United States--History--20th century. 4. Nuclear energy--
Research--United States--History--20th century. I. Ebinger,
Virginia Nylander, 1929- II. Title. III. Series.
QC16.B6575N67 2006
530.092--dc22

                            2005057959

Contents

Introduction: The Los Alamos Story

Near the middle of the twentieth century a small group of young people, most in their 20s and 30s, met on an isolated mesa far from the sights and sounds of the rest of the world. Working closely together for two and a half years on a secret, single-focus mission, they brought about the most significant technology of their century, creating a watershed event that would produce profound changes felt not only in their own country and at a specific time but in the entire world and for all time.

When their mission—to produce the atomic bomb that would end the war—was completed, many of the scientists and others who had done this work decided to stay in Los Alamos in what had been a muddy Army post beset with water shortages, difficulties in transportation and communication, inadequate housing, and other hardships. Those who stayed would be joined by others, and together they would create a community worthy of its first reason for being and of the natural beauty in which it was embraced. Business and medical people, teachers, construction workers, clergy, all joined the scientists in building schools and churches, a hospital, a library, parks and places for sports activities, businesses, streets, attractive neighborhoods.

The Los Alamos Historical Society has continued to collect and preserve memories and facts of every kind from the beginning—photographs, oral histories, physical objects, journals, reports. Now, in the late years of the twentieth century and the early years of the twenty-first, the Society's publications committee has set out on the journey to make accessible many of these facts and artifacts in a series of one-subject monographs grouped together under the title *The Los Alamos Story.*

Acknowledgments

*T*his book exists by the good graces of the Los Alamos Historical Society and the Los Alamos National Laboratory. I owe many thanks to both. While it does not complete The Los Alamos Story, *it adds an indispensable chapter that has been too long in coming.*

Members of the Society's publications committee, espcially Barbara Storms, Kyle Wheeler, and Jane Sherwood, gave continuing encouragement and much helpful advice and assistance. Rebecca Collinsworth, archivist for the Society, was invaluable in answering questions and in knowing just where to look for the photos I needed, as well as knowing about others I hadn't even thought of. Her skill in the ability to identify faces from old photos and to remember long-past events and dates is phenomenal.

The Laboratory gave permission to reprint much of the content of this book, articles that had appeared previously in Laboratory publications, and in providing many photos searched out from its archives by Dan Comstock, Alan Carr, and Gloria Sharp. Those three deserve extra thanks for patiently answering questions as well as finding photographs. Gloria deserves special thanks for her ready and ongoing artistic and technical advice. It was she who gave us the template on which each of the monographs in our series is based, and she prepared the cover for this book.

Thanks also to the many individuals who volunteered bits and pieces of knowledge about Norris Bradbury and the

Bradbury years. David Thomson and Helene Suydam, as well as my own sons John and Michael Ebinger, were among those. Other conversations or interviews with them and with Betty Lilienthal, Françoise Ulam, Fabiola C de Baca, Louis Rosen, the Rev. Colin Kelly, and Robert McGee were extremely helpful in providing insightful information.

Finally, many thanks go to Jim and David Bradbury for their continuing help with facts and family photos and their interest in seeing this book completed. A sad occurrence during the preparation of the book was the death of their brother John Bradbury.

vne

Prologue

*J*essie Siegel, a music supervisor in the Los Alamos
Schools, invited the young music teacher, new to
town in 1954, to her home in Western Area to meet
two returning music teachers, Marge and Lois, and two
other women interested in the music happenings of Los
Alamos, Kay and Françoise. They talked, found common
ground for plans for the upcoming school year. The four
veterans were filling the newcomer in on the music scene
when suddenly, bursting through the back door, through
kitchen and dining room, into the living room where they
sat, there appeared a bundle of energy in the form of a
man dressed in work khakis.*

*Lois introduced him, "...my husband Norrie." Sparkling
blue eyes, firm handshake, a quick smile. After a few
pleasantries and with a rapid-fire question asked of and
answered by his wife, he was gone as quickly as he had
come.*

*I was that new teacher. On the way back to my apartment
in the new kitchenette buildings on 9th Street I figured
it out: They were Lois and Norris Bradbury. (Lois later
swore she never called him "Norrie.") The other music
teacher was Marge Allbee, wife of Superintendent of
Schools Lewis Allbee. The other women I learned later
were Kay Mark, wife of Carson Mark, and Françoise
Ulam, wife of Stan Ulam.*

*From that time until his death in 1997 and Lois's a few
months later in early 1998, I was one of the many Los
Alamos citizens who admired and respected the Bradburys and who were honored to be among their friends.*

Norris Bradbury was a simple man, and humble. He washed the dishes in his kitchen and took out the garbage. He served his guests at regular welcoming parties for new staff members. He dug in his garden and worked in his woodshop. There is the story that the wife of a new-hire had a problem with the thermostat in her government-owned house. She called Zia, the end-all, be-all, fix-all housekeeper of early Los Alamos, and she was told that a repair man would be out soon to take care of the problem. Meanwhile, Lois had asked Norris to deliver a message to this Los Alamos newcomer. Norris, in his standard off-work attire, khaki shirt and pants, arrived first, before the repair man. But how was the householder to know? She simply assumed that her request had been quickly answered, so she explained her problem to Norris; he fixed it; then he gave her Lois's message. About this time the Zia repair man showed up.....

Stories of the kindness and helpfulness of Norris Bradbury abound. Lois taught piano at the Bradbury home to a number of children. Once a young student, leaving after a lesson, heard an unwelcome sound coming from his bicycle. Luckily for the boy, Norris heard it too and, covered with wood chips and sawdust, rushed out of his shop to investigate. "Let me try that out," he told the boy, and he took a spin up the long driveway and back. "Just a minute; I have an idea." Norris dashed into his shop and back out immediately with an adjustable wrench that he applied to the offending brake, and sent the boy safely on his way.

To know the story of Norris Bradbury, one must also know Lois; the Lois who, as a music teacher in Mesa School, once had to call in for a substitute because she was entertaining that day the Queen of Greece. The next day she was back at school, unshaken by her encounter with royalty.

And his story must also include his family, sons James, John, and David. James and John came to Los Alamos as young children with their parents; David was born here—in Box 1663 of course. They attended Los Alamos schools—Mesa, Pueblo, the high school.

Lois enjoyed telling the story of how the older two boys once played William Tell while they were baby-sitting their much younger brother. When little David balked at his brothers' commands, she said, Jim and John tied him to a tree and at least threatened to shoot him with their toy bow and arrow sets. All three survived the incident.

Oldtimers remember seeing Jimmy and John, while David was still too young to join the enterprise, pulling their red wagon loaded with vegetables from Edith Warner's garden, selling them to housewives hungry for fresh produce.

A high school teacher many years ago remembers an incident relating, he said, to Norris's character and his son John's. "I was a fly on the wall in the cafeteria line a few places behind John and a friend who proposed that they cut classes after lunch and resume an authorized dig they had at Bandelier. He added that 'your old man could cover for us.' I waited for John's response. He said it was tempting, but 'I don't think so—you don't know my dad.'"

As you read the first five sections of this book, you must be aware that each was written many years ago, yet each is presented in present tense, as if it were happening today. Two of the sections are essays with some insights into Bradbury's personal life as well as his life at the Laboratory. Two are transcripts of press conferences he had called in the face of events important in the life of the Laboratory. The last is a long conversation involving six of his friends and colleagues and their recollections of their years with Bradbury as leader of the Laboratory.

At the end of the book you will find a very short bibliography and a glossary containing names of all the persons mentioned in these chapters, as well as a short explanation of the scientific terms and acronyms referred to.

Many of the persons mentioned are now deceased; some of them have been for a very long time. The little boys have grown up, one of them now also deceased. The Laboratory has increased in size and in scope and has even changed its name more than once, from the Los Alamos Atomic Bomb Laboratory, to Los Alamos Laboratory, to Los Alamos Scientific Laboratory, and finally to become the Los Alamos National Laboratory. The military post has become a small city of some 18,000 residents. Its natural beauty, defined by heavily forested mountains, was assaulted in 2000 by a devastating fire that consumed in its furious attack on 47,000 acres not only the forests and the habitat they had provided for animals and birds but also the homes of some 350 families.

Many changes have occurred in Los Alamos and its Laboratory since the first of these articles was written in 1952. The town, once a compact community of government-built and -owned houses now has many spacious, privately built homes mixed in among many remaining original Los Alamos homes. Businesses have come and gone. The Laboratory has continued to expand in area as well as in personnel and activities.

The Bradburys and most of those who lived and worked here in the earliest days of the Manhattan Project are gone. But the legacy of Norris Bradbury will be a part of the Los Alamos story from now on.

vne

Mister Los Alamos
1952

by
Al Rosenfeld

This story appeared originally in 1952 in the Empire Magazine of the Denver Post *and later in* Reader's Digest. *It was reprinted in* LASL Community News *on October 20, 1960, in honor of Bradbury's fifteenth anniversary as director of the Laboratory.*

Every morning Norris Bradbury clatters off to work in a decrepit Model A Ford which the family calls "the town car." His good-humored blue eyes are serene as he stops to pick up a load of children on their way to school, then stops again to prop open the ancient trunk lid with a stick to make room for still another load of shouting youngsters.

Yet this wiry, youthful-looking fellow chugging along at a slowpoke pace is probably under as much pressure as any other single individual in the country. In the key job he holds down for the University of California as director of the Los Alamos Scientific Laboratory—the most vital of all the nation's A-bomb installations—Dr. Norris Edwin Bradbury is responsible for keeping the United States ahead in the field of atomic weapons.

The position calls for rare qualifications. The man who fills it must be scientist, administrator, diplomat and handler of community problems, business executive, and public servant of the highest caliber. Norris Bradbury is all of these. He commands the respect and admiration of congressmen, generals, and topflight scientists. And his immediate associates feel toward him a deep personal loyalty and devotion.

Not more than a handful of living human beings have contributed as much to the maintenance of this country's scientific defenses as "Mister Los Alamos."

Yet the average American has never heard of him. Even in nearby Santa Fe it is not unusual for someone to say to him politely, "Oh, you work at Los Alamos?"

Two-Fingered Staccato

If you ask Bradbury's secretary how her boss operates, she will reply crisply and promptly, "With speed." Even the inter-office memos he knocks out with two staccato fingers on his antiquated Remington emerge with astonishing rapidity. "You never saw a man go through a basketful of papers so fast," she says admiringly, "and you'd swear he wasn't reading even a fraction of the stuff. Yet, six months later, he'll remember every detail."

At home he operates with the same wasteless precision of movement. "He's calm and cheerful enough about it, goodness knows," explains his wife, "but everything he does—washing dishes, serving guests, gardening, anything—it's always zip, zip, zip! He lives as though he were killing snakes every minute of the time. And when night comes, he passes out as soon as his head hits the pillow. That's probably all that saves him."

As one of his staff observed, "It isn't so much Bradbury's speed that amazes; it's the way he manages to find time to do everything—and to do it gracefully. He's simply a wonderful-all-around human being."

From the Navy to Los Alamos

Now only 43, the California-born Bradbury has always moved fast. A prodigy in physics and chemistry, he made Phi Beta Kappa and graduated summa cum laude from Pomona College at the age of 20, then went on to get his Ph.D. at the University of California. In short order he became recognized as an expert in such fields as atmospheric electricity, the properties of ions, and the conduction of electricity in gases.

When World War II came along, the Navy assigned Commander Bradbury to its research center at Dahlgren, Va. Since he felt he was doing important work there, Bradbury was not too happy when orders came through transferring him to an isolated, unheard-of, mesa-top base in New Mexico. "I did all I could to get out of it," he now admits, "without, of course, knowing what I was getting into."

Admiral W. S. (Deke) Parsons with Bradbury. "We asked the Navy for Bradbury....we got Bradbury. (LANL photo)

But higher-ups knew—they had planned it that way. When a technical crisis arose," recalls Rear Admiral W. S. Parsons, then at Los Alamos, "we asked the Navy for

Bradbury. By decision of Admiral King, we got Bradbury—and he did such a fine job that when Oppenheimer departed after the war, Bradbury was appointed director."

It was then, back in October of 1945, that Norris Bradbury made his big pitch for the United States of America. Dr. Robert Oppenheimer, the Laboratory's guiding genius, had just left, and Bradbury accepted the temporary directorship for a six-month period prior to returning to his teaching post at Stanford and the new home he had bought at Palo Alto.

There was no official provision of any sort for the continuance of a government-sponsored atomic program, and many felt that this would be a mere mop-up operation. "Los Alamos," commented one well-known scientist as he prepared to go, "will remain only as a monument commemorating man's inhumanity to man."

Is the Laboratory Obsolete?

The country was in a sweetness-and-light mood. The war was over, the United Nations had been launched with apparent success, and people were writing their congressmen to bring the boys home and disarm, for now there would be only love and peace in the world. And of what use was an obsolete item like an atom-bomb base?

Bradbury did not share the prevailing mood. He knew that Russian scientific research must be going ahead full-blast and was alarmed at the possibility that postwar America, in its naïve over-optimism, might blithely let the USSR get the atomic jump on us. He felt strongly that the job remaining at Los Alamos was much more than a six-month close-down operation. With so much more important research work crying to be done, it was unthinkable that Congress would condemn the best-equipped atomic Laboratory in the world to a career of gathering cobwebs.

Inwardly Frantic

He felt confident that legislative machinery would be set up to answer the nation's atomic-defense needs—Oppenheimer was in Washington working hard on exactly that problem. But how long would it take?

The youthful director. (LANL photo)

At the Laboratory all was uncertainty and confusion. More and more scientists were packing their belongings—often with great relief—and heading back to their more comfortable university positions or to more profitable ones in industry. Some were morally shocked at having participated in the A-bomb's creation and were now washing their hands of it. Others didn't like the super-secrecy and physical inconvenience that came with living on "the Hill."

Meanwhile Bradbury was inwardly frantic at the thought that if the wholesale exodus of scientists continued, the Laboratory would simply die of inertia. A persuasive talker in his quiet way, he communicated his fears and convictions to a handful of his staffmen, who agreed to hang on a while longer. He enlisted the aid of Maj. Gen. Leslie R. Groves, who stuck his neck out to the extent of authorizing a permanent housing project.

With many scientists still vacillating and the atomic tests at Bikini already scheduled, Bradbury delivered an ultimatum: pack up and go, and we'll pay your way home; otherwise, stay and get down to the big job that has to be done. Many went—but enough stayed on to form the skeleton crew that kept the kettle boiling until a reawakened Congress, under the farsighted leadership of the late Brien McMahon, passed the atomic energy act.

Harried as he was by a complexity of problems during those chaotic days, Bradbury managed to keep the atomic program moving ahead. The tests at Bikini in May and July of 1946 came off without a major hitch—partly because, in many cases, Bradbury disregarded seniority and jumped bright young men into top positions of responsibility. Some of his associates still regard the success at Bikini as little short of miraculous.

Higher Pay Scorned

Once over the hump, the Laboratory has never again been anything but a steadily progressing organization. Today Los Alamos is a thriving, populous city and county of the state of New Mexico, with atomic research its only indus-try. Most of the men who stuck with Bradbury during that rough time-of-transition are still with him.

They make up his trusted "first team." All have received offers from outside at double the salary which Brad-bury—restricted to the university's faculty salary scale— can afford to pay, but there have been no resignations.

Bradbury attributes the steadfastness of his old staffmen to patriotic motives and to the fact that Los Alamos is getting to be a nicer place to live and work all the time. "It's seldom that a man leaves our employ because he is unhappy with his job. My big worry is that his wife will be unhappy—because she is too far from the super-markets or the movies, or because her home isn't nice enough, or because she doesn't think the schoolteachers are any good, or any one of a dozen other things."

Once, when the government wrote a new lease agreement for housing facilities—something the AEC considered a routine matter—a storm of protest over the new provi-sions swept the city. Bradbury, who was off at another A-base, had to be called back in a hurry. By the time he arrived, things were in a state of near riot, with personnel threatening wholesale resignations and departures.

With prompt and decisive action obviously necessary, he closed down the Laboratory, called a mass meeting, and, in a matter of hours, had listened to grievances, answered complaints, made notes of the valid objections, pointed out those he thought unreasonable, and ordered a new lease written up and submitted to Washington.

*Living conditions in the early days on The Hill left a great
deal to be desired. The plan for new and better housing may
have influenced many to stay. (LAHS photo)*

*Bradbury, General Leslie Groves, Eric Jette examine plan for
construction of Lab sites and permanent housing. Standing: Colonel
Lyle Seeman, Colonel E. E. Wilhoyt. (LANL collection, LAHS)*

No Room for Frills

While Bradbury looks after the comfort of those who
work for him, he frowns on frills and "extras." He keeps
all his buildings and installations free of expensive
trimmings, and has often cut out big items that have
already been approved by Washington. Recently he elimi-
nated plans for an elaborate air-conditioning plant in a
new office building. "It's pretty cool for us in here. We
can just keep the windows open," he said.

Bradbury's chief information officer suggests that his
great success might lie in some of the things he does not
do. He does not, for example, believe in issuing directives
and regulations. When Washington's demands along these
lines get burdensome, he drops them a short note: "We do
not intend to comply."

Another thing Bradbury does not do is place any censorship restrictions on his scientists. They are free to give
talks or deliver papers at their own discretion, without
submitting them to him for approval. "Any man trustworthy enough to work here," he reasons, "is trustworthy
enough to exercise his own good judgment."

All One Working Family

Nor is anyone at the Laboratory allowed to be conscious
of rank or position. "We're all one working family," he
insists. "Nobody around here is called Doctor or General
or anything but Mister—unless you call him by his first
name. It's true that our principal job involves the military

applications of atomic energy, but, while we get along fine with the Army, we try to run Los Alamos as little as possible like a military base."

His evenings at home are almost as busy as his days at the Laboratory. He's an excellent handy man (he used to build houses with his father), and loves to fix whatever's wrong around the house. He builds things with his two older sons, John and Jimmy, in the carpentry shop, takes the "town car" apart and puts it together again, works in the garden, helps Lois in the kitchen, and is constantly entertaining newly arrived staff members to make them feel at home.

Rare, brief vacations are spent in Mexico. Bradbury is an amateur archeologist and likes to dig around the ruins of ancient, old-world civilizations as a change from thinking about the new ruins that atomic weapons might create. But even on these jaunts, he still zips from one place to another, and zips back to his work in a hurry.

Runners in an Atomic Race

The Bradbury marathon is a purposeful one. As one of his fellow scientists points out, "He set a pace for us. We're in the position of Olympic runners in an atomic race. If we let up for a minute, the other team might overtake us. And in this race, that would be disastrous."

Even that outspoken critic of the Atomic Energy Commission, Senator Hickenlooper, more than once has emphasized the fact that his criticism did not include Norris Bradbury and his Los Alamos Scientific Laboratory. "You and your group out there," said Hickenlooper to Bradbury during a joint Congressional committee hearing, "have done a grand job, and I think the country owes you a vote of thanks for the long years of devotion that you have given to this great subject."

If our atomic progress still outpaces the world, it is largely due to the vision and drive of Norris Bradbury.

Bradbury Answers
Unfair Charges Against
Los Alamos Scientific Laboratory
1954

*I*t was 1945. The war had ended. Euphoria had
swept across much of the nation. The servicemen
were coming home, many Los Alamos scientists were
returning to their teaching positions in universities across
the country, others resuming their education that had
been interrupted by the war. The Laboratory had come
under new leadership: Oppenheimer had gone back to
California; Bradbury had struggled successfully to mobi-
lize and re-direct the Laboratory's efforts to maintain the
nation's nuclear capability.

*Now fast forward to 1954. Far from remaining idle in
the intervening years, LASL in 1946 and 1948 conducted
tests in the Marshall Islands, Operation Crossroads
in 1946, and the Sandstone tests in 1948, leading to
improvement and expansion of the nuclear stockpile.
During this time, and actually in Los Alamos since 1943,
research on a hydrogen bomb continued, but as a long-
range project secondary to the immediate need to produce atomic weapons to end the war, and now, after the
war, to maintain a position of strength.*

*In September 1949 the USSR, aided in its design by
secrets stolen from Los Alamos by Klaus Fuchs, detonated its first atomic bomb. This was enough to push
US government officials and politicians, as well as
some scientists, into a hasty decision to concentrate on
the "Super," and in January 1952 President Truman
announced, "I have directed the Atomic Energy Commission to continue its work on all forms of atomic weapons, including the so-called hydrogen or super bomb."
This was in effect a full-steam-ahead mandate, and Los
Alamos was quick to comply. "Mike," the first hydrogen
bomb, was successfully detonated at Eniwetok by LASL*

scientists on November 1, 1952. Although it was not an actual weapon, its success proved that thermonuclear fusion was possible.

The Hydrogen Bomb: The Men, the Menace, the Mechanism, *written by journalists James Shepley and Clay Blair, Jr., appeared in 1954 and immediately found a wide and interested audience. In tracing the development of the Super, it made innuendos and direct accusations against LASL for "unnecessary delays" in making the H-Bomb, for dissention and confusion of policy, for dragging its feet in promoting this "essential check on communist aggression," even for disloyalty.*

In answer to these charges Norris Bradbury read the following statement to reporters.

vne

In late 1945 a small group of courageous and loyal scientists and technicians undertook to continue the post-war operation of the Los Alamos Scientific Laboratory. These men believed that atomic weapons development had barely begun, that other countries would develop such weapons, and that the safety and security of the United States—if not of the world—depended upon the technical lead of this country. These men had the courage to stay at Los Alamos in the face of an uncertain future. The Atomic Energy Commission did not then exist. Job offers from universities and industry poured in upon them. Their home-towns seemed preferable to the strange surroundings of an isolated military post. The most senior scientists of the war days felt that their responsibilities required their return to their university posts. Younger men were leaving to return to school or other jobs. But some men stayed—and built a Laboratory.

These men did not make demands nor require promises. These men stayed and built the greatest weapons laboratory this country has ever known. These men stayed and developed the geatest array of powerful and flexible atomic weapons of any country in the world....developed them faster, developed them where they were urgently needed and requested by the Armed Forces....developed them to fit the productive resources of the newly established Atomic Energy Commission. They stayed and built a Laboratory that developed every successful thermonuclear weapon that exists today.

Others left, but these men stayed and worked, and many others came to join them. What these men accomplished cannot be told in detail, for these facts are classified **top secret.** These men do not talk. They believe in deeds, not words. But these deeds earned for the Los Alamos Scientific Laboratory the only Presidential Citation ever awarded to any laboratory for its extraordinary success in the development of both fission and fusion weapons, and its contribution to the collective security of the nation and the free world.

What these men accomplished was this: They built a Laboratory from 1,200 employees in 1946 to 3,000 employees in 1954. They brought back many of the senior wartime staff members as consultants, frequently for months at a time. They worked and thought and had ideas. In the fission weapons field, they advanced development from the few primitive wartime weapons to weapons enormously more powerful to weapons enormously cheaper; to weapons so enormously more efficient that only a small fraction of the bomb load, and a small fraction of the number of planes, and a small fraction of the cost in fissionable material were required. They multiplied the atomic capability of this country in so many ways that not even billions of dollars spent in active material production would have been equivalent.

Nor was the Laboratory idle in the thermonuclear field. The wartime efforts of a small group of men in the Laboratory were summarized in the 1946 conference. Later in that year, the basic idea for one of the present patterns of thermonuclear weapons arose, although no way to exploit it effectively could then be seen. An elaborate program of basic research, both theoretical and experimental, was undertaken in order to provide both the necessary fundamental data for the basic calculations as to whether the "super" bomb would work at all, even if it could be ignited.

1946 Nuclear Physics Conference at Los Alamos to discuss thermo-nuclear work carried on during years of World War II and the future possibilities of fusion weaponry. Front row left to right: Bradbury, John Manley, Enrico Fermi, Jerry Kellogg; among those also shown are Gregory Breit, Robert Oppenheimer, Richard Feynman, and Jim Tuck. (LANL photo)

Thermonuclear work never stopped. Basic nuclear data were obtained, **top secret** theoretical studies on thermo-nuclear processes were carried out, the great electronic brain, the MANIAC, was being built with such calculations in mind, and simultaneously the necessary practical studies of materials and potential engineering problems were conducted. All this is in the official record of the Laboratory's work during the period from 1946 to 1951. Thermonuclear work grew as the Laboratory grew. By 1949 the design and understanding of fission bombs had proceeded far enough to permit studies of their applica-tion to thermonuclear systems to be undertaken. Even before the Russian bomb was fired, the Laboratory was working on the detailed design of an experiment employing thermonuclear principles that would answer some (but far from all) of the basic questions regarding thermonuclear systems. Still later events suggested the addition to the Greenhouse program of even a more elaborate experimental approach. In March 1950 the Laboratory went on a six-day week for almost three years to speed its developments while it was further expanding its scientific staff.

Had the Laboratory attempted to exploit the thermonuclear field to the exclusion of the fission field in 1946, what would have happened? Hypothetical history can only be an educated guess, but the guess in this case is almost certain. The fission weapons stockpile would have been but a fraction of its present size. The essential fission techniques required for practical thermonuclear weapons would not have been developed. Discouragement would have nagged at those who worked in a field without the means for practical accomplishment, and the program—and the Laboratory—might have died. Rather than delaying the actual accomplishment of thermonuclear weapons, the Los Alamos Scientific Laboratory has, by its insistence on doing necessary things first, demonstrably provided the fertile soil in which the first feasible ideas could rapidly grow, and demonstrably did develop such weapons, and probably, but not demonstrably, did so years ahead of any other course that could have been pursued with the facilities and people available. Technically, the development of fusion weapons is so inextricably allied with and dependent on the development of fission weapons, that great success in the former had to follow success in the latter.

The assertion that the Los Alamos Scientific Laboratory was reluctant to work in the field of thermonuclear
weapons is false. Although the thermonuclear program is
referred to in every program of the Laboratory from 1945
on, some statements are of particular significance.

In a top secret letter to the Atomic Energy Commission
dated December 9, 1949, three months after the Russian
explosion, the Laboratory stated over my signature:

> We propose to augment to the greatest
> extent possible the effort devoted to research
> on the problem of attaining a nuclear reac-
> tion involving the light elements. The goal
> of this effort will be an experimental test....

The goal stated of course is classified, but was attained
even earlier than we then believed possible. In another
section of the same letter the statement is made:

> The importance of these questions (thermo-
> nuclear) makes, in our opinion, an under-
> standing and test of the basic phenomena at
> the fastest practicable rate imperative. Then,
> and only then, can the many issues be
> resolved without recourse to hypothesis or
> wishful thinking.

In another letter to the AEC dated November 17, 1950,
over my signature, the Laboratory's position was stated
unequivocally:

> The importance of arriving at firm conclusions
> regarding the application of these or other

potential thermonuclear techniques to military use makes it imperative that vigorous work be continued in this field.

The letter, classified top secret, went on to give several pages of description.

At every stage from 1946 to the present time, the fission and fusion programs—both in basic research and in practical application—were pursued with the maximum appropriate emphasis, with care, with precision, and with success. What "might have been" is idle speculation. What would have happened to World War II if the Manhattan District had started work in 1939?

The imputation of disloyalty to that now large group of scientists and technicians who are fundamentally responsible for the atomic weapons leadership that this country presently enjoys, and who are dedicated to the continuance of this leadership, is a tragic, if not malevolent, thing. The motives behind these accusations of Los Alamos are unclear; their bases are faulty and irresponsible information necessarily obtained from those who do not and cannot know the classified facts; and their effect on the Laboratory would be wholly disheartening were it not for our knowledge that the facts warrant the full confidence of the nation in our accomplishments over many years.

Press Conference
on the Nuclear Test Ban Treaty
1963

Norris Bradbury
Arch Napier, *Time*
Frank Morgan, UPI
John Marlow, Associated Press
John Young, LASL Public Relations
Norman Thomas, Santa Fe *New Mexican*

*T*he Cold War was raging in 1958. President Eisenhower had announced a moratorium on testing
nuclear weapons, a unilateral ceasefire, but with
the understanding that the USSR would also honor and
participate in it. In 1961 the USSR broke the moratorium
with a series of large nuclear explosions. The US immediately resumed testing also.

Tensions escalated in the early 1960s. The Cold War continued; Russian Premier Khruschchev displayed angry
outbursts in United Nations sessions; the Berlin Wall was
erected in 1961; the Cuban Missile Crisis occurred in
1962.

President Kennedy continued President Eisenhower's
initiative to control nuclear testing worldwide, and after
years of negotiations, the USSR agreed to join the US and
the UK in the Limited Nuclear Test Ban Treaty that would
allow underground testing but no atmospheric, underwater, or outer space testing.

Immediately after the Treaty was announced by President Kennedy on July 26, 1963, Norris Bradbury called
a press conference to explore its effects on work at Los
Alamos Scientific Laboratory. A transcript of that press
conference, slightly edited for clarity, follows.

vne

Bradbury: My purpose in suggesting that we get together and talk about this is that I recognize all of you and all of the community have questions as to what the proposed nuclear test ban treaty might actually mean for this Laboratory. Before I can do that in detail I would like to give you some ideas of what the Laboratory does; also, to make very clear in my opening remarks here that after I get through with those, you will be quite free to ask me questions. Some of them I can try to answer, some I may have to say: look, I'm sorry, that certain discussion is either classified or beyond the scope of the Laboratory's problem, but I will do my best for you.

The first thing I want to make clear is that test bans, test moratoria, are hardly new and surprising. We have seen them before. This is not a complete test ban being proposed. It is a test ban only on atmospheric, underwater, and outer space shots. The President in his remarks last night made it quite clear that nuclear testing underground could continue. In other words, this is not a complete change in what we have been doing. As you know, we haven't tested in the atmosphere for something on the order of a year now, in the Pacific last summer; we've been testing in Nevada, and if the treaty went into effect today, our actual day-by-day life would probably not particularly change. So, the first point I want to make, in general, is that this is not a catastrophic difference in our mode of operation. It is a change, yes, but I will discuss some of the ways the change might occur and some of the ways it might make an even stronger Los Alamos over the course of the next 10 or 20 years.

Other Nations Involved

Let me start out, therefore, by going into a little history. The Laboratory, I think, realized—and I have said this publicly a number of times—after the development of the hydrogen bomb in 1951 and the years following, it became quite clear that there was a brand new area of energy release open to us that would be made use of. It was also clear that we had other nations in the atomic energy business, and it became quite clear that some day the countries of the world would have to find some method, if nuclear catastrophe was to be avoided, of eventually getting out of nuclear war. The concept of nuclear war, we know, is almost too horrible to be easily contemplated. The atomic bomb made war bad enough, but the hydrogen bomb made it a thousand times worse. The Laboratory, being somewhat optimistic, really believed, then and now, that eventually a way would be found out of the nuclear war impasse; a sidetrack from the path to the edge of the cliff of destruction would be found. It is possible, as President Kennedy suggested last night, that a first step in that direction has been taken.

LASL Broadens Its Base

When we deliberately looked into the future we decided to broaden the base of the activities of the Laboratory. Up to that time almost all our work was either fundamental research or specifically directed at weapons activities, but in early 1952, following the success at Los Alamos with the hydrogen bomb, we quite deliberately undertook to take our specific talents, facilities, ingenuity and various technical fields which had been relevant to the weapon development program and explore their relevance to peaceful uses of atomic energy. Most of those are known to you. We have a very active program, for example, calling upon a lot of our skill in plutonium technology in the use of reactors for the production of power. And we are specializing in two areas—one of these is in very high temperature gas-cooled reactors, to some extent a sort of derivative of our Rover program which I will mention in a moment, and liquid plutonium reactors, which are direct consequences of the fact that Los Alamos has probably the greatest skill in plutonium technology, particularly metallurgy, of any place in the world.

I think everyone realizes that unless the world can eventually learn how to burn ordinary uranium, uranium-238, instead of just uranium-235, which is only a fraction of 1 per cent of the uranium we mine, fission power will never really have a profound impact upon the power needs of the world. Therefore, one must learn to burn 238. There is a way to do that; it's called breeding. But breeding means the production of plutonium, and then you have to burn the plutonium. And that's the real reason we are interested in the use of plutonium as a reactor tool, a reactor material. I mentioned Rover. We got in the Rover business because it became very clear, with the development of hydrogen bombs that intercontinental ballistic missiles began to make some military sense. They could deliver a bang big enough that the errors of delivery would not nullify the virtues of a whole mission. At that time, strange as it may seem, chemical motors for big intercontinental missiles weren't very well developed. There was even a question as to whether they could be. We recognized that nuclear power for this purpose would be harder and longer, but it was a second string for the bow, and if there were chemical troubles we could probably help out.

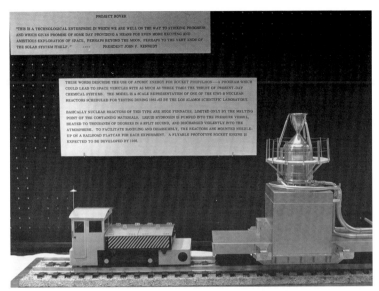

A model of Rover. The banner at top left reads as follows: "This is a technological enterprise in which we are well on the way to striking progress and which gives promise of some day providing a means for even more exciting and ambitious exploration of space, perhaps beyond the moon, perhaps to the very ends of the solar system itself. President John F. Kennedy"   (LANL collection LAHS photo)

President Kennedy, shown with Bradbury and Senator Clinton P. Anderson, visiting the Rover program in 1962. (LAHS photo)

Bradbury and Stan Ulam (back to camera) in front of the Kiwi reactor at the Rover test site. (LANL photo)

Role of Nuclear Rocketry

It soon became clear that the real role of nuclear rocketry was in space. If you use it on the surface of the earth you are sending a man to do a boy's work, and furthermore, the chemical people have done an outstanding job in developing chemical motors. So Rover is now a very important part of the long-range space program, which as you know is one of the national programs with the highest priority. Paralleling the similarity to the correspondence between an atomic bomb and atomic power was the question: Is there any correspondence between a fusion bomb, or hydrogen bomb, and fusion power? Well, there is a correspondence in the fact that they use the same sort of materials, or could, but the technical correspondence is entirely different. Nevertheless we are working very hard with a vigorous program, one of the most versatile in the Commission, on how you might some day make thermonuclear power. We have an active program in biology and medicine, a growing program. It's a very important field in national science these days, that probably as a field has more consequences to human welfare per dollar expended than any other field one can imagine. Physicists, mathematicians, chemists, are all taking an active part in the biological research program of the Laboratory.

Underlying all these activities is of course a basic program of fundamental research, research that parallels the facilities that we had to have for the weapon development, but which is not necessarily now directed to weapon development, but is characteristic of the tools that we have and the excitements of modern physics, modern chemistry, metallurgy, the competition of techniques, hydrodynamics, mathematics. We even get into

Arthur Murray synthesizes a compound labeled with carbon-14 to be used for treatment of some types of lymphatic cancer. (LANL collection LAHS photo)

astrophysics. As some of you may or may not be aware, two of our men interested in astrophysical problems, on their own with a Laboratory loan of equipment, went to Canada to make some observations of the recent eclipse. So we don't quite have an eclipse expedition, we have a part of one. The Laboratory has a wide variety of interests and basically the weapons business is now only a part of our activities.

Weapons Money and "Other"

I would like [you] now for a moment to think of the work of the Laboratory as a sort of pie diagram, and if we draw a line roughly down the middle of this pie, half of it, about 50 per cent—not exactly because these things never scale quite accurately between dollars and people—but about half the work of the Laboratory is financed by

UHTREX reactor core being lowered into its containment vessel. (LANL photo)

weapons, what is called weapons money, money under the control of the Division of Military Applications of the Atomic Energy Commission. The balance is financed by other parts of the Commission, primarily the Division of Reactor Development but some by the Division of Research and some by the Division of Biology and Medicine. I will simply call this "Other," but it includes a large piece of Rover, it includes a large piece of reactors— the plutonium reactor, LAMPRE, and the UHTREX reactor; Sherwood, biology and medicine, or biology research. This combination of things here is roughly half the total program of the Laboratory.

But let me point out that my position for a long time, in fact since the start of the Laboratory, is that about half of this money that supports the Laboratory which comes from the Division of Military Applications goes to basic research. It supports all our physics, it supports almost all our chemical research, it supports all our computations research and our mathematics and our hydrodynamics; it supports our astrophysical activities; it supports our Vela Hotel, Vela Sierra activities. So a large part of this is just plain research. It could be supported by somebody else, too, but it's just plain solid, good research and we are looking for ways to expand it. We have some hope that one of the tools to be expanded here one way or another will be the addition of a very large accelerator on the Los Alamos scene. So this is just plain research, this quarter of the pie. In this balance of the pie the research activities and the development are more directly related to weapons and so this can be called research, and development directed to weapons. And then you come down here to specific weapons, when you have to make something for somebody—we do, at least we make the prototype. We do no manufacturing, of course, but we do specific weapon development. Here's the point then, and this might be then called something that has to do with the future and tests. So you see that what we are talking about, where this treaty might affect the Laboratory, comes down to this rather small area.

Testing in Weapon Development

Now, I want to say a few words about what testing means in the course of weapon development and what the progress of weapon development really is. So again this picture is in focus. Weapon development starts from a series, and a rather small series, of fundamental ideas about nuclear explosions. Two of the fundamental ideas were developed in 1943 and 1944. The brilliant ideas of Stan Ulam and Edward Teller to make the fusion reaction possible in a weapon form is another unique and brilliant idea. The remainder of the problem is essentially adaptation, variations, extensions and refinements of a rather few fundamental concepts. There is a great deal that we can do, and we have done it, without actual testing. The first thing we do is have an idea, how we can extend it to make it better. We want to get, let's say, a weapon that is more efficient, is smaller, or has a larger yield, or gives economy of fissionable material, or any of the things that go to make a weapon a part of a weapons system. And people will put their heads together and think we might be able to push it a little bit further that way; we have an idea if we did this we could make that possibly work a little better. Or we make an involved series of calculations, an involved series of experimental tests in the Laboratory, without resorting to a fission or fusion reaction, but very complicated technical experimental observations in and around Los Alamos; around in the sense that at GMX Site, S Site, and various of our experimental sites you carry on these experimental explorations to see whether your idea has anything in it to make it better. All of these things, of course, occur all the way through here; it goes on. Eventually you come to the place where you say: look, I've carried this about as far as I think I can and now I ought to test it.

Well, tests themselves can occur in a variety of forms. It isn't always necessary to test things at their optimum dimension, maximum dimension. One can test it in some cases piecewise. One can find out things about the system without necessarily resorting to a complete full-blown, super-duper nuclear explosion. As long as we can carry out some aspects of the test program we can make a great deal of nuclear progress and indeed this is what we do in testing in Nevada. We find out a lot of things, sometimes about complete systems, sometimes about parts of systems. It is an essential part of our trade, quite frankly, to be able to test. It's a very important part of our trade. But to have to test it at what I would say full-scale, whatever that word means, to be able to test at full-scale is not always completely essential. So that with a capacity to test underground, atomic weapon development will continue.

And, as I mentioned in my opening remarks, it is very clear the President pointed out that underground nuclear weapon testing, certainly contained, could continue. It's clearly written down in the treaty, if you look at it, the objective is to lay the groundwork for all testing to cease. If all testing were to stop, and it's a big "if," even so, nuclear weaponry does not stop. Admittedly, if you have a bright idea and you calculate it out with experiments in the Laboratory, work on it and so on, and you can't test it you aren't very likely to try to extend it very much further, because if it doesn't work when you try it out you would like to know that before you make the next extension of design. So if there is no weapon testing whatsoever, forward progress in terms of greater ingenuity, greater versatility, is probably likely to come to a premature close, although there will be challenges of course to see what you could still do then. We went through a period, you will recall, between 1958 and 1961, when we did not test at all and yet we made very significant weapons progress in that time and we surprised ourselves even, by seeing what we could do with experimental techniques, by calculation techniques, by people just beating their heads against the wall.

Stockpiling and New Military Systems

Let me come back to specific weapon development. There are still two types of things that have to go on and probably will go on until the happy millennium comes when nuclear weapons are abandoned. One of these is taking care of the stockpile, the care and feeding of the stockpile of weapons. Ninety per cent or a little more of the weapons in the stockpile are of Los Alamos origin. The atomic weapon business has gone on here for a long while. These are very involved technical systems, atomic weapons; they have new materials, strange materials, exotic materials, requirements of very great precision of character and behavior; you can't let them get moldy or rusty and things of this sort.

We suspect as well that before weapons are abandoned, when and if they are abandoned, there will be new military systems. It becomes a truism to say that an atomic bomb is no good unless it can be delivered. And the role of the delivery vehicle or the delivery system is just as important, sometimes indeed it can be more important, than the weapon or warhead itself. And we expect there will be new requirements and new missiles, new types of bombs, new types of warheads, new types of military requirements that we will have to meet. And we can meet these, we'll meet them with what I call interpolative designs. In other words, if I have made and tested a bomb, of one size, weight, or something, and somebody wants a bomb within these specifications, fine; I'll make it for them. I may not know its precise yield, but I can be certain it will be between this one and that one, and I will be certain of its size and I will be certain it will work; these interpolative bombs won't represent any extension of weapon technology, but they may represent in terms of the weapons system an enormous extension in defense capability. And this sort of thing could and would go on, whether or not there were weapon testing in any form. Well, this is perhaps enough to give you the impression that when we can't test we are somewhat handicapped, but if we can't test in the air we can test underground; the handicap is considerably less, we can still progress. Even in the long run, if we couldn't test at all the effect on the Laboratory's total program is in a small area.

What I am endeavoring to do, and with this I will close my remarks, is to make it clear to you two things: One is that atomic weapons are only a part of the Laboratory's activity; we have many other things that excite us, important to us and to the country, have active Washington support. The other is that atomic weapons are still a responsibility. This responsibility can be exercised by testing underground and even in the long-range, if the hope of the President expressed in the treaty becomes true, the Laboratory will still have a responsibility in the weapons business until atomic weapons are ultimately abandoned.

I think it would come as no surprise to any of you to know and have me say that Los Alamos has no fondness for atomic weapons per se; people in the Laboratory don't work on atomic bombs because they like to kill people. They have only worked in this over the last 20 years because we thought in some way it provided a strength for the country to avoid war, to bring about, ultimately, as there seems today to be a start, a step toward the abolition of war. Literally a small step, but I think everyone will agree it is a positive one. Thank you. Now, I'm at your service.

Arch Napier, *Time***:** Could you tell us which part of the pie the care and feeding of the stockpile fits into?

Bradbury: In the weapons side. I want to make that point. It is important; it's an important responsibility. It is not a very time-consuming task today; the stockpile seems to be extraordinarily well made and it turns up with almost no troubles. It's our responsibility to make sure there are no troubles.

Frank Morgan, UPI, Santa Fe: As a result of the proposed treaty and progress it's made, are there any immediate changes contemplated in Los Alamos?

Bradbury: Well, none of which I am aware and none that I would see to be necessary. In the first place, the treaty has not been ratified. Secondly, if it were ratified today or tomorrow, actually there would be no change; we aren't testing in the air today. I can't tell you what our plans would, or would not, have been because that is obviously classified, but if the treaty went into effect today it would merely perpetuate what we have been doing for the last year. So a change in our day-by-day activities clearly isn't indicated. Naturally our *planning* for future test operations will change, but that's planning; our preparations will change; perhaps we will have a longer time scale or something. As the President said, he intends to prepare and he intends to plan in case things fall apart. And that's part of our responsibility, to plan and prepare. Those things will not change; we've been doing it. I foresee no changes in our activities that are a consequence of this particular day.

John Marlow, Associated Press: Would your underground testing in Nevada be stepped up any because of this ban?

Bradbury: That's a question which is beyond my capability to answer. You see, the scope of underground testing is determined by the availability of dollars; it has to be approved by the Commission, by Washington, and we naturally press for as much as we can do. How much we can actually get will depend upon national policy and national dollars and things of this sort. We've been working at it, and I would not suppose this would change. This remains to be seen.

Napier: In point of fact, during the last test ban did the Laboratory reduce its work force or its budgets?

Bradbury: It grew.

Napier: Was this because of some big new things, like Sherwood?

Bradbury: No, no, it was not, it was not.

Napier: Did the weapons side grow?

Bradbury: Right, right. It grew because we did just what I told you earlier. We said, look very hard at what you can do by what we call laboratory techniques. One of the consequences of that was a very large gadget that I will

PHERMEX, Pulsed High-Energy Radiation Machine Emitting X-rays, used to study the behavior of nuclear weapons without actual testing. (LANL collection LAHS photo)

simply call PHERMEX—I don't know how many millions of dollars are involved—which is just a laboratory technique, in which you can explore without going to nuclear explosions, some of the problems that are associated with some of the hydrodynamics of weapons. This was the time in which we got STRETCH, the big computing machine; if you can't do experiments in the nuclear field, then you see how far you can stretch your theory, your calculation ability, to prove that it's going to work. We actually grew; I can't give you the precise figure; I don't remember, but the business did increase somewhat.

Napier: Did you find it hard to recruit good personnel during that time because the nation probably thought you were shutting down?

Bradbury: Well, they didn't seem to think we were shutting down then as much as we are now, that we would sell the community, that we are being disposed of. That seemed to get the most national response. No, I think it must be admitted that nuclear weaponry is not regarded across the country with the greatest of enthusiasm. Nevertheless, I am always extremely pleased and surprised and grateful at the number of highly talented, ingenious and versatile physicists, mathematicians, chemists that see a

Programing room of STRETCH, the giant IBM computer, largest in the world in the early 1960s. (LANL collection LAHS photo)

national requirement here, a national need, and feel a sense of both interest, excitement and patriotism, or loyalty, or responsibility. It is possible to recruit outstanding, excellent people in the weapons industry. I think they feel this is something the country has to do.

Napier: Was there any special problem during the last test ban?

Bradbury: I would say no greater problem than there ever was; in fact there was a certain challenge because you couldn't test. What could you do without testing? How certain could you be of a system that you might put in the stockpile if you hadn't actually tested it?

Napier: Do you anticipate any problem if the treaty is ratified and there is a limited test ban this time in getting people or in keeping people?

Bradbury: No more so than we have had or have. Again let me point out that at this point we are doing exactly what we have been doing for the last year. We're testing. I haven't been told to the contrary, and the President made it pretty clear, I thought, that underground testing was part of the present role. He looks forward to its abolition eventually. But not today. So this is the point I keep insisting on—today the situation is not changed by the existence of the treaty. You are doing tomorrow essentially no different than you did yesterday. Until we find some new set of rules, that's the business. It is a major step, well it's a step and perhaps a major step in a sort of public impact. It is the first time that Russia and the United States have been able to get together in a tangible way to make a tiny step toward some form of international agreement in the weapons field. And that step is probably a very large impressive one, although the technical step itself is small.

Morgan: Following this up, Dr. Bradbury, while you are still able to test underground, just what limit on weapons development will the treaty have, what do you get out of an atmospheric blast that you can't get underground?

Bradbury: Well, there is one thing you can't do underground that is of interest to people, and of importance. We have done a lot of it in the past and it's just a question of debate as to how much you know and how much more there is to know and that is the question of weapons effects, effects of a nuclear explosion in the atmosphere, or in space. You are aware from our last summer's activities that a number of bombs were shot off fairly high, here and there. They were seen in Hawaii. This is a type of observation, a type of experiment, you can't make underground. So that, you simply can't do. Otherwise you probably can do almost anything you want to and could afford. But if you ask me to make enormous nuclear explosions underground, within the limits of the treaty, which says no fallout beyond the territorial limits, then it becomes an awfully expensive, difficult, slow process. You'd have to dig such a deep hole that you wonder how many of these you can dig per year or per national· budget, or something. So it's, I think, fairly obvious that you tend then to look at smaller systems or the smaller parts of large systems, but this depends upon how much money you are willing to spend for containment.

Morgan: On the technical or principle level of nuclear blasts, whether underground or atmospheric, correct?

Bradbury: I don't quite understand what your question implies.

Marlow: Well, just the experimentation with weapons, whether it's in the air or whether it's underground.

Bradbury: Weapon development per se, nuclear warhead development per se, can take place either way. The techniques of diagnosis are slightly different; the results of the diagnostics are essentially the same. Some things are more easily done in air, some things are more easily done, frankly, underground. Underground testing has some nice virtues, curiously enough.

John Young, LASL Public Relations Office: Would it be safe to say that when we do have a test, say on a tower, a lot of experiments in more or less pure physics research are made possible that wouldn't otherwise be, and you get a lot of other people involved in making measurements?

Bradbury: But that's also true underground, John. There are some very fine experiments being done underground that are just plain pure physics. What was the experiment down at Carlsbad called? Gnome. Gnome had a lot of just good beautiful physics in it. That's what it was, an underground experiment. It wasn't weapon development. It was a nuclear physics experiment.

Young: I was speaking of the manpower question. A lot of people from other divisions flock around to make measurements, taking advantage of these phenomena and then go back to their regular work.

Bradbury: Yes, this is a nice point. As long as one is able to set off bombs underground or anywhere else, they provide the physicist, experimental research physicist, with a most remarkable source of radiation, neutrons, temperatures and pressures that exist outside of the solar system, or in the solar system. It's comparable with astrophysical temperatures and pressures. And there are some very nice experiments that one can do and these get done. This is the scientific side of the Plowshare program. Now remember that the Plowshare business is defined as the peaceful uses of atomic bombs, for digging ditches, mining, digging canals and so on. It also has a very definite interest just as the scientific applications of nuclear explosives. We call this Project SANE. We could use these things to try and make very heavy elements, in neutron spectroscopy, if they want to do experiments in pressures and temperatures that no one else has available. And I believe that this type of experiment, many of them, can be done as well, sometimes a little better, underground than they can in air. Other types of experiments you can do better in air, but you do what you can.

Napier: From the point of view of the universities that in basic, pure research, hitchhike on things like Gnome, does going underground mean higher budgets and higher costs?

Bradbury: The government generally has provided the basic cost of getting the hole. The universities don't have to dig the hole. The taxpayer goes into the hole.

Napier: Within the bounds of security, can you discuss what the effect of the package of this limited test ban might be on our research in anti-missile weaponry?

Bradbury: Well, not very easily, but let me just make a general statement here. Anti-missile weaponry is rather more a problem of a missile system. It's devoted to detection, analysis of the direction of the incoming missile, a command and control system to get your attacking missile up there in time, at the right time and at the right place. This problem is 99 per cent one of missiles, and missile control, missile detection, and 1 per cent a problem of nuclear weapons. Now it is not devoid of problems to nuclear weaponry, but I think if the other people in the missile business can take care of theirs, we can take care of our side of it. It's an area where you don't need big explosions anyway, you don't want to attack an incoming missile with umpty-ump megatons; you attack it with a smallish type of warhead that has to come fairly close. You arrange to get my warhead there, I'll have my warhead ready for you.

Marlow: Can you carry off enough experiments underground to determine whether your bombs are getting any cleaner?

Bradbury: This is an area of research that one can do underground, yes. I don't know that I like your phrasing; our bombs aren't getting cleaner, we make them cleaner, they don't do this by themselves. But that's an area of technology that can be explored depending upon what sort of problems you're looking at and what money you want to spend. It adds some problems when you go underground, but it also takes away some.

Napier: Los Alamos has been active in several of the Vela programs to detect sneak tests. Are we in a better position now to detect cheating under this treaty than we were during the last test ban?

Bradbury: That's a technical question in the intelligence business, and I think I had better duck it.

Norman Thomas, Santa Fe *New Mexican*: Will the test ban change personnel, like will weaponry personnel be replaced by someone else? Will it effect a change on the people in the community?

Bradbury: No, I believe not. Not at all. Let's recall one thing here. The people who carry out my weapons tests are also the people who worry about my Rover testing in Nevada. You remember I made the remark that we will certainly have, from the President's remarks last night, a program of preparedness, of preparation, planning and the research and the techniques of weapon diagnostics and research in the techniques of these scientific applications that I mentioned. That work will go on. And so your people who might be overseas next year, or next two years, or sometime, will be doing other things, but they will be in this other field.

Napier: Actually, the Test Division may not reduce in size or even be transferred within the Laboratory at all?

Bradbury: Look, the Test Division has always been busy in Nevada. We haven't tested in the air for a year. And we've been busy. We have our hands full right now as it stands. I want to make a point very clear. This treaty does not change tomorrow as opposed to yesterday.

Young: I might point out, Arch, that when we do go to testing overseas, the Test Division goes on a 54-hour week, which is not all the hours they work either. They go on seven-day weeks, and on crash programs.

Bradbury: Ordinarily, overseas we cut down enormously on our activities in Nevada. We just can't run them both simultaneously.

Young: And you have the support of 20 or 25,000 military people. They are the ones who also have other things to do. They are called in when the tests are going on, they go back home when they are not. It doesn't really affect the total manpower situation much at all.

Bradbury: The tests are really run by a Joint Task Force, as John says, in the tens of thousands. We don't actually have very many people in the field. Some of the work is done by contract, a lot of it is done by other areas—the diagnostics for military interests, and so on. Even that limited demand on us, though, generally means that we have had to put things off.

Thank you.

Ratification of the Treaty

*I*n *July 1963 the USSR agreed to negotiate the Limited Nuclear Test Ban Treaty, and in early August the treaty was signed in Moscow. The Senate Foreign Relations Committee, the Armed Services Committee, and the Joint Atomic Energy Committee set up eleven days of hearings in mid to late August to determine whether the Treaty should be ratified. Leading scientists from around the country, as well as political leaders, were called to testify. Leading the opposition were Edward Teller and John Foster, both from Lawrence Livermore National Laboratory, and conservative Senator Barry Goldwater, but Bradbury's eloquent testimony and other scientific evidence were persuasive in the committee recommendation and the Senate's vote of 80-19 on September 24, 1963, to ratify the Limited Test Ban Treaty, a history-making document that was the first step toward and the framework for the Non-Proliferation Treaty of 1968.*

A clear and detailed account of the LNTBT's progress and ratification can be found in A Guide to the Nuclear Arms Control Treaties, *a Los Alamos Historical Society publication by David Thomson.*

The concluding paragraphs of Bradbury's presentation to the Senate follow:

"If we do, indeed, vigorously prepare for atmospheric tests resumption; if we do, indeed, continue an active program of underground testing, then I believe that the Los Alamos Scientific Laboratory can maintain a vigorous, enthusiastic, and productive group of scientists engaged in weapon development. We have met this challenge, and harder, before when we did not test at all for the three years after 1958. I find in my people a response to a challenge to see what can be done within one limitation or another. The consequence to this challenge has always been that more can be done than one at first may believe. I think it will be so in the present case. I think, in this instane, I may speak for most of my colleagues at Los Alamos. We have never believed that nuclear weapons were an end in themselves; they are merely tools to an end—the strength of the United States—a strength to prevent (or if necessary to win) a war—but whose ultimate goal may be the abandonment of war and most of all, a nuclear war.

"To Los Alamos, and I think I speak for the majority of my staff, this treaty is a small but positive step in that direction. It has risks—but we believe thay can be minimized by testing underground and preparing for tests above ground. It is the first faint sign of hope that international nuclear understanding is possible. We would far rather count on that hope than on the opposite. If now is not the time to take this chance, to count on this hope—what combination of likely circumstances will ever produce a better time? I, myself, with considerable knowledge of nuclear things, with some knowledge of their military use, but with only a plain citizen's feelings about people and nations and hopes and fears would prefer to try to follow the path of hope."

vne

A Quarter Century of Fun
1970

by
Kenneth Johnson

This story appeared originally in
The Atom, *Volume 7, Number 8,*
September 1970, a publication of
the University of California, Los
Alamos Scientific Laboratory,
Office of Public Relations, PO Box
1663, Los Alamos, New Mexico
87544.

A new hire's wife picked him up in front of the administration building after work. As they drove around the quadrangle, he said, "There's the director of the Laboratory." "Where?" she asked while scanning the sidewalk as if expecting to see a man with a sandwich board reading: "Norris E. Bradbury, Director, Los Alamos Scientific Laboratory." "That fast-walkin' guy wearing the 'Truman' shirt," the new hire replied.

At 61, the tall, balding, quiet-voiced Bradbury does walk fast. But then, he does everything fast. He even talks fast. As director of the Laboratory, a post he relinquished effective September 1 after a quarter century, he went through paperwork and other workday chores with miraculous speed. But, at the same time his work was done with meticulous confidence and scalpel precision. Former secretary Hazel Clancy once said, "You never saw a man go through a basketful of papers so fast. You'd swear he wasn't reading even a fraction of the stuff. Yet, six months later, he'll remember every detail."

According to his wife, Lois, he is the same at home. "He lives as though he were killing snakes every minute of the day," she said. "Whatever he's doing—washing dishes, gardening, home repairs—it's always zip, zip, zip.

"Even when we travel," she said, "he's no different, especially in a new country. The first thing he does when we get there—that day if there is time, or the next morning if there is not—is to check the transportation system. He takes whatever buses go in all directions and then he comes back and says, 'We'd better look at this, this, and this.'

"After being married to him for 37 years, I've learned that I can go my own pace. I like to stop and look along the way and I know there'll come a time when he gets far enough ahead of me, that he'll look around and wonder what happened to his little woman. Then, he'll wait for me to catch up."

Bradbury's son John and John's wife recall a time when they planned a short vacation with "father." "Vacations with Norris are full of rapid movements over long distances; few people travel longer to stay less time. It's almost as if getting there is all the fun." They had planned to meet Norris in Cartagena, Colombia, on a certain day. "John and I flew down from Miami, but the connections Norris had went to Bogota, then back to Cartagena." The younger Bradburys arrived in Cartagena first. "We waited and waited, left messages at the hotel desk, but no Norris. We learned that the flight he was on sometimes flew Bogota-Barranquilla, or once in a while Bogota-Cartagena, but all that was last year and 'things had changed.'

"At dusk we left Norris to make the trip as best he could and looked about the town. If a Bradbury says to meet at a certain place at a certain time that's what he means. We had done our part; we were there. It was sad to think that poor father was slipping or that some fateful event had changed his route.

"He arrived about midnight—probably a few minutes before for the record. Somehow he had gotten the last jet to Barranquilla. His pilot was new, didn't realize how long it takes to stop a jet, and the short Barranquilla runway was not quite long enough. But they stopped, coasting onto a beach and nearly into the mangroves.

Norris got the last taxi in town too, I guess, and coaxed the driver to Cartagena.

"Norris and John went out for a quick beer, and the next day we set out to visit the old city. Sunny weather turned into rain of the most plenteous and permanent kind. Norris, never stopped by a little (or a lot of) rain, took us out to an old whitewashed Spanish fort where the 18th-century Spanish galleons assembled. We admired it in the rain—we were the only ones to do so—and the lining and glue fell out of John's hat.

"Now did Norris think this adventure was a loss? Not in the least. He had survived a jet landing by a new pilot, outwitted the local travel system and even beat time (by minutes), arriving on the appointed day, and he saw a quaint city in a splendid tropical rain."

"I guess I'm not a very good sitter-arounder," Norris Bradbury said. "I like to cover a lot of ground generally. I'm a nervous tourist."

He does sit around some, however. He reads a lot and, as might be expected, he does this fast too. According to his wife, he reads a lot of technical publications, although in the past few years "he's become extremely curious about other things. He's been reading Charles Dickens lately, even on the plane when we go somewhere."

Bradbury also has other leisure time interests. He is an amateur archaeologist and has made several trips to Mexico where he plies this skill. "I acquired a taste for it by living in New Mexico. There are a lot of old sites around here. Our middle boy at one time thought he wanted to become an archaeologist and I traveled around Mexico with him.

"We usually just cover the roads in Mexico. I have a great interest in visiting the Sierra Madre country; it's peppered with old sites and we have friends there. I like it; it's a change, a different environment, and it's on the way to Guatemala, British Honduras, and other places we've visited. It suffices my taste to go somewhere new."

Bradbury also enjoys caning. Much of his wickerwork has been the making of new seats for some of the straight back chairs in his home. He also makes some of his own furniture and does minor construction projects and repair work in his home. His workshop equipment includes band and circular saws and a small wood lathe. "I get a great deal of pleasure working with wood; I've taken some pictures of benches and beds and other things at the Museum of New Mexico and copied them. I made beds for our grandchildren. They're colonial style. This means they're not very elegant. A blind craftsman can probably do as well with a dull jackknife," he said with a smile that is spontaneous and often.

As late as the 1950s Bradbury drove to work in a non-descript Model A Ford, picking up children along the way and taking them the rest of the way to school. He was known as "Mr. Los Alamos" (and still is) and the old automobile was known as "the town car." Taking the old car apart and putting it back together again was something he and his sons enjoyed doing together. "It became harder and harder to keep it running so I finally gave it to the Santa Fe High School auto shop. I replaced it with a pickup. I drove the truck to work and all over the Mexican mountains. I've had a pickup ever since."

Bradbury's wide interests and his restless urge to accomplish quickly and with precision whatever he sets out to do is apparently a part of his heritage. His father, Edwin Pearly Bradbury, has always been "whatever he wanted to be," Bradbury said. "He went to the University of California for approximately a year in about 1902, but he didn't stick. He almost went to sea, but he got a bad cold and the ship went without him. In the early 1920s he was a city electrician in Santa Barbara. While climbing a pole he was badly burned when he was working on something and the power, which should have been off, wasn't.

"After he got married he went into the nursery business. He became a landscape architect and practiced in Hollywood. He got tired of that, as he frequently got tired of everything he did, and went to Fontana where he took up ranching. He lived there until about 1935, a rancher. At one time he had some grape vineyards and grew cactus commercially. Well, then he moved to Pasadena where my mother, Elvira Clausen Bradbury, was brought up. To amuse himself he took a machinist course at night. He was a machinist for years at Cal Tech and worked on the 200-inch Palomar telescope. He realized he wasn't getting any younger and retired in Santa Barbara. Now he makes clocks; he has a house full of clocks. He makes them in a nice little shop there. After he retired he served on the City Planning Commission in Santa Barbara for years.

"My father was always a nervous reader and had a terrific memory. He is linguistically skilled. He speaks good

Spanish and a bit of French. My mother was a school
teacher. She pretty much stopped teaching when she got
married and had children. She served on the school board
in Fontana, but in those days it wasn't so easy to work
and raise children. We didn't have frozen TV dinners and
so forth."

Bradbury was born May 30, 1909, one of four children.
His sister died in infancy, and his parents adopted twins.
"Bobby," he said, "works at an Air Force base in Ama-
rillo, Texas, and has something to do with the rehabilita-
tion of helicopters for Vietnam. Betty is chief operator for
the phone company in Pasadena and has been for years.
Both of them served in the Marine Corps during the war."

Bradbury attended Hollywood High School and then
Chaffey Union High School in Ontario, California. He
was graduated from Chaffey at the age of 16. "I graduated at 16 because when we moved from Hollywood to
Fontana, there was a difference in the school years, and
birthdays I guess made some difference. Anyway, as I
recall, I needed a year and a half of school to graduate.
We moved there in the spring, and if I didn't graduate
a year from the following June, it would have been two
years. So, that summer I took some extra courses and finished up in one year."

Bradbury went to Pomona College in Claremont, California, and graduated summa cum laude in 1929 with the
B.A. degree in chemistry. His scholarship earned him
the Phi Beta Kappa key. Why chemistry? Bradbury said
he had a chemistry set when he was about 12, as most
youngsters do, but the primary reason was an interest in
math and science formed when he was in high school.

"In those days," he said, "you went to college to learn
to make a living. You took courses you thought might
get you a job. Math and science are what I enjoyed in
high school. English and history were courses you took
because you were supposed to. What else could I do?"

It was at Pomona that Bradbury met the girl who would
become his wife in 1933. "Lois was the sister of my
roommate at college. She was engaged to someone else.
The engagement fell apart and I moved in," Bradbury
said.

"I was an English literature major in college," said
Lois. "When I first knew Norris we were both working part-time to get through school. He worked behind
a soda fountain that was owned by a redhead named
Daisy. He used to make an ice cream concoction called
the 'mudroll.' It was called that because it was in a college town and every year the seniors would initiate the
freshmen by rolling them in the mud. Norris was a good
worker even then. Daisy even offered to make him a part-
ner."

Under other circumstances Bradbury might today be
a big man in the ice cream industry, but his life didn't
unfold that way. While at Pomona he became intrigued
with physics. He did his graduate work at the University
of California at Berkeley where he served as a teaching
fellow from 1929 to 1931 and a Whiting fellow during
1931-32. In 1932 he received a Ph.D. in physics for his
work on the mobility of ions in gases. That same year he
was awarded a National Research Council Fellowship in
physics.

Edwin Pearly Bradbury, Norris's father, a man who "has always been whatever he wanted to be." (Family photo)

*A very young Norris Bradbury with his mother, Elvira
Clausen Bradbury, about 1910. One recognizes the same
eyes and smile that were evident many decades later.
(LANL photo)*

Sixteen-year-old Norris Bradbury, the young motorcyclist in southern California in about 1925. (LANL photo)

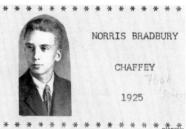

Bradbury as a high school student, left and above. Identification card for Chaffey High School. (LANL photo)

*Phi Kappa Alpha, social fraternity at Pomona College,
in 1928. Bradbury is at extreme left on third row from
the bottom. Second from left in second row is Duncan
MacDougall who would become leader of GMX division
at LASL. At extreme right of top row is Robert Platt, Mrs.
Bradbury's brother and Norris's roommate. (LANL photo)*

*Norris Bradbury and Lois Platt
on their wedding day in 1933.
(Family photo)*

*The young couple at home
in the early days of their
marriage. (Family photo)*

"When I got to Berkeley," said Bradbury, "I was assigned as a reader to Professor Leonard B. Loeb who taught sophomore classes in physics." Bradbury was considerably influenced by Loeb during these years of his life. He did his thesis under Loeb's direction and started his military career at the professor's suggestion. "Loeb had been in World War I and was a naval reserve officer. He suggested that I apply for a commission and I did. My ensign's commission was signed by a lieutenant commander by the name of Nimitz who was professor of naval science and tactics at Berkeley at that time. I went to meetings once a month and on cruises in the summer. I was an engineering officer; I liked the hot, foul-smelling steam machinery that was below the deck of a destroyer. At Loeb's suggestion I became an ordnance specialist, and I was that until I retired from the active reserve."

After graduating with a Ph.D. in physics, Bradbury spent the next two years doing research at the Massachusetts Institute of Technology. In 1935 he was named assistant professor of physics at Stanford University. He had already established a reputation as an expert on conduction of electricity in gases, properties of ions, and atmospheric electricity. He published numerous technical articles on these subjects in journals such as *Physical Review, Journal of Applied Physics*, and *Journal of Atmospheric Electricity and Terrestrial Magnetism.*

"About 1940 all reservists were put on notice. I'd been in about 10 years then, and I was called up in early 1941. The Navy let me stay on at Stanford for the academic year, and I started doing work that would be relevant to what I would be doing in the Navy. I was assigned to the US Naval Proving Grounds at Dahlgren, Virginia.

When I got there, I didn't do what I thought I was going to do. Rather, I was assigned to work in exterior ballistics—what happens after a projectile leaves the muzzle of a gun. Projectiles were getting faster and faster, and ballistics and firing tables weren't very good. The first round from a gun muzzle might be its last, and it was necessary to hit the target the first time. So, this is what I worked on.

"Loeb was at Dahlgren and so was Parsons (then Captain William Parsons who was later associate director at Project Y). In mid 1943, Parsons 'disappeared.' About a year later, I 'disappeared'; Parsons had come to Los Alamos and he sent for me.

Los Alamos from the air. (LAHS photo)

"I hadn't had any leave since I'd been at Dahlgren, so I was given 10 days or two weeks in June 1944. We were visiting my folks in California when I got a telegram from the Navy saying my leave was canceled. I was to be met in Albuquerque, according to the wire, and I was: Parsons met me at the train. I recall spending two or three days here; I stayed in the Parsons' house."

While Bradbury was at Project Y, he was told why he was wanted there, but he wasn't over-enthusiastic about the proposal. "Parsons told me, 'If you don't want to come, don't come.' I thought to myself, 'If this works, we'll never get out of it,' and I dragged my feet.

"I met Lois and the kids somewhere on the way back to Virginia. We had two sons at the time—John and Jim— and Dave was on the way. In Chicago my conscience got the better of me. I got to thinking about the blue uniform I was wearing, and who was I to argue about where I was assigned? I called Parsons and told him I'd take the job.

"I took Lois and the kids back to Virginia to pack up. Then, we started out with six well-worn tires and discarded them as they wore out on the trip up here, and I didn't have any more gas coupons when I got here. We could get tires then and we were given gas coupons enough so we could get to Santa Fe once a month. People got together for trips, so we got to Santa Fe now and then.

"At first we lived in one of the Sundt apartments which have since been torn down. They had showers but no bathtubs and were over-heated with coal-driven furnaces, but lasting friendships developed there.

The Sundt apartments were sought-after housing in the early days of Los Alamos. Each building had two apartments upstairs and two downstairs. (LAHS photo)

The Bradburys' second home was on Bathtub Row, formerly the Arts and Crafts house at Los Alamos Ranch School. (LAHS photo)

*The third Bradbury home—their real home for the rest of
their lives—nestled in giant ponderosa pines and low piñon
and chamisa. The "Porta Potty" indicates the house and
the neighborhood were in the construction stage. Note "the
town car" in the far right center.*

"Later we lived in one of the houses on Bathtub Row (so-called because they were the only houses at Project Y with bathtubs). It had been the arts and crafts building for the Ranch School and had been divided into two homes. It became vacant and I applied for it. Oppie (Oppenheimer) said I could have it if Fermi (Enrico Fermi who achieved the first sustained nuclear reaction) didn't want it. Fermi said he didn't want it because it was rumored to be a cold place to live."

During the war years when scientists at Project Y were developing the atomic bomb, the best technical personnel available were being recruited from universities and industry with desperate rapidity. "I guess I was picked for the Project because I had worked with Parsons, had had some chemistry, was a physicist, I knew a little about nuclear physics, and I had had some ordnance experience at Dahlgren," said Bradbury.

One of the many military personnel assigned to the Project, Bradbury was placed in charge of the implosion field-test program. He later headed the assembly of all non-nuclear components of the implosion nuclear device.

Project Y efforts progressed to the point where scientists were faced with the question of whether there was any basic flaw in the concept of a nuclear explosion. If not, the gun-type design was essentially certain to work, but the implosion idea (a subcritical mass of plutonium compressed to super-criticality by high explosives) had many technical problems. If an implosion system could be tested successfully, the gun design was bound to work too. This test—named Trinity—was conducted July 16, 1945, near Alamogordo, New Mexico.

Bradbury, in recalling his experiences at Trinity Site, said, "Several months before the actual test there was a 100-ton high-explosives shot scheduled for the purpose of calibrating instruments and taking other measurements that would help us in organizing for the Trinity event. We in the explosives division had a direct interest in getting that shot set up and detonated. As I recall, it was sometime in April that we went down there to set it up, and this was my first introduction to the site. It was hot, dry, and dusty; tracks in the sand were the only roads. We were living in 16' by 16' hutments which were also hot. The only thing pleasant about the place was the beer we drank.

"There was nothing to do there but work; there was nowhere to go. The road getting in there was rough, and security between Los Alamos and Alamogordo was extremely severe. We were forbidden to stop anywhere on the road between these places, although we probably did stop for a meal, but we were careful about it.

"After the 100-ton test we started to organize for Trinity itself and I was assigned responsibility for developing the procedures and for supervising the assembly of the device, except for the nuclear components which were to be put in at the base of the tower at the site. I was to develop the SOP's [standard operating procedures] to get the thing on top of the tower and to finish assembling it up there.

"It was quite a little undertaking that started back here (Los Alamos). We had a dry run in assembling it in a building that is still here at S Site to be sure the thing would go together. We put it together without the final nuclear parts. A hole was left so that the nuclear components could be inserted later.

"We loaded it on a five-ton truck and three or four days before the actual test date we started out for Alamogordo. At the site we parked the truck in a building overnight and the next morning went to work at the tower. We backed the truck under the tower, lifted the assembly off the truck with a hoist mounted at the top of the tower, pulled the truck out, and lowered the device on the floor. We were scared to death that we would drop it because we didn't trust the hoist, and it was the only bomb immediately available. It wasn't that we were afraid of setting it off, but we might damage it in some way.

"We set it in a cradle on the floor and then the boys from the ranch house (the MacDonald ranch house served as assembly headquarters for the nuclear parts) came over to put the plutonium in it. For a while there was a good deal of consternation because when they first tried to put it in, the damned thing wouldn't fit! As it turned out, the problem was simple: the plutonium was hot and had expanded. After some cooling down, it did fit just as it was supposed to.

"We plugged the hole then with the rest of the HE blocks and buttoned it up. We began to hoist it up the tower and this is where we were really scared because if we had dropped it, we might have had a catastrophic mess on our hands. So, we lifted it a few feet and put several layers of GI mattresses all over the floor of the tower. Then we hoisted it through a hole in the floor at the top of the tower, replaced the floor and set the bomb down on it.

"Well, the worst was over, except it was a 100-foot walk up the tower; there was no elevator, just a ladder on one side, and it was hotter than hell in July. Some of the boys went up to put on the detonators and some other diagnostic stuff, and that was, for the most part, the end of my job there.

"We didn't trust the detonators very much so we had a lot of diagnostics connected with detonator behavior and, of course, there were a lot of other experiments there to diagnose the bomb's nuclear behavior. If there was a failure in the system we would have some way of knowing what it was that failed.

A thoughtful Norris Bradbury beside the Gadget at the Trinity tower, 1945. (LAHS photo)

"The firing date was delayed, maybe a day, because a diagnostic cable broke. We had to find it, dig it up and fix it. It didn't have enough slack in it when they laid it in the trench and covered it up, so the weight of the dirt broke it. It was a small crisis, and I don't remember that there were any others of this type.

"A day or two before the Trinity shot we had an important Laboratory experiment up here (in Los Alamos). It was designed to test the behavior of a system like the one at Trinity. But we couldn't make any sense out of the results; they were either very bad or they were uninterpretable, so we decided to ignore them. All of our previous experiments indicated we were on the right track. It

July 16, 1945. (LANL photo)

wasn't until several months later, we found the experiment had serious flaws; it couldn't have told us anything, it didn't tell us anything, and we were quite right to ignore it."

On the night of July 15, when Bradbury and other scientists and military personnel had finished their jobs, they went to sleep on hillsides several miles from ground zero. It was cold and there was a drizzling rain. "The weather was so dismal, we didn't expect the shot to go that night and we were tired," Bradbury said. "I didn't know it was going to go until about five minutes before it did. Somebody woke me up—I don't remember who—and I just had time to get out of my sleeping bag and to face away like we were told to when it went off.

"A lot of us compared what we saw, what we felt, and what we heard with the 100-ton shot, and we made guesses among ourselves on the hillside out there about the yield of the bomb. Some of us thought it to be about 10 kilotons. Other guesses ranged from 5 to 20 kilotons.

"For me to say I had any deep emotional thoughts about Trinity...I didn't. I was just damned pleased that it went off." In retrospect, Bradbury said, "Most experiences in life can be comprehended by prior experiences, but the atom bomb did not fit any preconception possessed by anybody. The most startling feature was the intense light.

"One thing I've never understood, never tried to—I drove into the yard at home, got out of the jeep, and Lois came out the back door and said, 'Well, it worked, didn't it?' It had been an undercover operation and, of course, you never told your wife anything, and possibly no one did, but our success had gotten around up here pretty fast."

Mrs. Bradbury well remembers the incident. "Everybody was going up in the mountains to see something. Mrs. Ed McMillan and I both had young children and we couldn't find any baby sitters. We were frustrated because we couldn't go. So, we took turns going out once in a while to see what we could find out. Finally, Mrs. Parsons called us and told us that whatever it was, worked. So, when I went out the back door and told Norris, 'It

Bradbury with General Leslie Groves, accompanied by Protective Force personnel, 1946. (LANL photo)

worked, didn't it?' I didn't know what it was that had worked. It just seemed like a good idea to say it."

Following Trinity, the atomic weapons "Little Boy" and "Fat Man" were completed at Los Alamos and then dropped over Japan. The war ended in the fall of 1945 and technical activity at the Laboratory slowed. Universities and industry, whose staffs had been seriously depleted by wartime efforts, were rebuilding. Many scientists had standing offers to return to their pre-war jobs and even those who didn't were made offers that included tempting sums of money. The University of California which had accepted operation of the Laboratory in wartime gave no indication that it was willing to continue its operation. The future of nuclear energy was just as uncertain and the gloom precipitated faster when Oppenheimer announced in October of 1945 his intention to resign the director's post.

"About 4 p.m. one afternoon, Oppie called me in and asked me if I'd be willing to take on the directorship," Bradbury said. He had contacted Groves (the late General Leslie R. Groves, director of the Manhattan Engineer District) and I don't know who else.

"I was anxious to get back to Stanford, but I said I'd think about the offer. I talked to Lois, Fermi, and others to see what they thought of the idea."

It was then that Bradbury made his "six months" statement in which he agreed to be the director of the Laboratory for six months, or until such time as a permanent man was found—whichever came first.

In October of 1960, Oppenheimer was among the many
well-wishers to congratulate Bradbury on his 15th year
as director of the Los Alamos Scientific Laboratory. In a
letter to Bradbury, Oppenheimer wrote:

"It was fifteen years ago that you and I first talked of the
possibility—to me the desirability—of your taking over
the direction of the Los Alamos Laboratory. I remember
your hesitations and your reluctant agreement to do it for
some six months.

"Even more, I remember your first visit to Los Alamos,
at the invitation of (then) Captain Parsons. More than
anyone else who came to Los Alamos, you expressed,
with force and eloquence, your misgivings about what we
were up to, and your reluctance to be involved in it.
Now fifteen years have elapsed, and you have earned the
respect, the gratitude, and the affection of the many men
and women who have worked in the Laboratory, and the
appreciation and indebtedness of all of us, both for what
the Laboratory has undertaken and accomplished, and for
the spirit in which it has done so. The seriousness with
which you entered on these responsibilities has contributed very much to the way in which you have met them."

Said Bradbury, "Groves confirmed the appointment.
Oppie wanted to leave right away, and I was still in the
Navy. Parsons got me out in nothing flat. I was at the sep-
aration center in Los Angeles from about 8 a.m. until 1
p.m. one day and that was it. I had 15 years in the service
then. Eventually I finished out thirty years in the active
reserve.

Until he found time to buy civilian clothes, Bradbury was forced to wear his uniform shirts without insignia. (LANL photo)

"For a while, I wore uniform shirts without an insignia. I didn't have much in the way of civilian clothes. But then, nothing was like it is now. Mail and Records consisted of a couple of filing cabinets in Oppie's office.

"The University of California wasn't asked about my appointment. I didn't know this until about two years later. The University almost threw in the contract." Many University officials met Bradbury for the first time after he had been appointed. Robert Underhill, vice president and treasurer emeritus of the University, who negotiated every contract for the Laboratory from its inception until he retired in 1963, remembers his first meeting with the newly-appointed director: "While I visited Los Alamos almost every month from March 1943, for over two years, I did not meet Norris until the day of the 'E' Award Ceremony after the war. My contacts had always been with Dr. Oppenheimer and his top administrative staff and the Manhattan District officers. The conscious and evident intent to keep me as an outsider from as many contacts as possible during the war were so effective I did not, at that time, see or even know of a Dr. Bradbury. My first knowledge of such a person was when General Groves took it upon himself to appoint a Dr. Bradbury as the University of California's project director. And so, University President Robert Gordon Sproul and those of us invited to the 'E' Award Ceremony met him on October 16, 1945."

The "E" Award was Army-Navy recognition of exceptional performance on the production front during wartime and was accompanied by the War Department Scroll. President Sproul accepted the "E" flag from Groves, and Oppenheimer accepted the scroll from Admiral Parsons. Oppenheimer's acceptance speech left a lasting impression on Bradbury. "The strange thing about that speech," said Bradbury, "is that Oppie made it, not quite on the spur of the moment, but with about five minutes thought. To my mind it was a touching speech, a very real one and a very true one. I'll always treasure it."

At that time Oppenheimer said: "It is with appreciation and gratitude that I accept from you this scroll for the Los

Alamos Laboratory, for the men and women whose work and whose hearts have made it. It is our hope that in years to come we may look at this scroll, and all that it signifies, with pride.

"Today that pride must be tempered with a profound concern. If atomic bombs are to be added as new weapons to the arsenals of a warring world, or to the arsenals of nations preparing for war, then the time will come when mankind will curse the names of Los Alamos and Hiroshima.

"The peoples of this world must unite, or they will perish. This war, that has ravaged so much of the earth, has written these words. The atomic bomb has spelled them out for all men to understand. Other men have spoken them, in other times, of other wars, of other weapons. They have not prevailed. There are some, misled by a false sense of human history, who hold that they will not prevail today. It is not for us to believe that. By our works we are committed to a world united, before this common peril, in law, and in humanity."

The following day, on October 17, 1945, Bradbury assumed direction of the Laboratory. "We weren't really doing much of anything very progressive then," Bradbury recalls. "What held the place together was the Navy's program to determine the effects of nuclear bombs against naval vessels."

The Laboratory had been informed of this test—called Operation Crossroads—in December of 1945. Preliminary meetings were held that month and in January of 1946 to set up a joint task force operation. The

Laboratory was to provide the atomic weapon and undertake the technical direction of the test.

"When we went to Washington," Bradbury said,"to talk to the task force people about Operation Crossroads, we flew from Kirtland in Albuquerque in an ancient B-29. It was one of those flights where the crew said, 'Thank God, we made it,' after takeoff. We were riding in the bomb bays of the plane. It lost an engine somewhere over the Mississippi River and then we lost half of another—the propellers couldn't be adjusted and it was running at about half power. The wind was blowing and it was snowing all over the country. The pilot was a nervous wreck. We had parachutes, but that wasn't very comforting because who would ever have found us in a snowstorm? Well, there was another passenger on board who had considerable experience flying B-29s and was apparently familiar with that part of the country. He thought there might be a chance of landing somewhere in Ohio. He took the controls from the pilot and took us in. He missed the runway on the first pass and made kind of a fighter-plane landing on the second. We bought drinks for everybody and took the train the rest of the way to Washington.

"That was the start of Operation Crossroads. When I came back from that trip, the water system in Los Alamos was froze up." The water line from Guaje Canyon remained frozen for several weeks. Tank trucks brought water from the Rio Grande to the community's old water tower. Some was put into the system and some was doled out to housewives in pots and pans. This event climaxed bitter resentment toward living conditions in Los Alamos and probably hastened the exodus of many persons already unhappy with community operations.

"Operation Crossroads came off in the summer of 1946," said Bradbury, "it gave me something to put people on and I needed all the good people I could get, so I said nothing that would rock the boat at that time. When I made my 'six-months' statement upon becoming director, I didn't think I wanted to be the director; I thought I wanted to get out. But I decided I couldn't run a Laboratory that would have a future unless I was willing to put my own future on it. It needed a man that believed in it himself before others could believe in it.

"After Crossroads I thought I could afford to lose those people who couldn't make up their minds whether they wanted to leave or stay. I made my so-called 'tree-shaking' statement then: 'pack up and go, and we'll pay your way home; otherwise, stay and get down to the big job that has to be done.' They'd all been hired during the war with the promise of return travel home whenever they terminated. What I did was to stop return travel as of a certain date."

Although Bradbury's staff had successfully completed its large part in the Crossroads test series, and he had now formed a nucleus of scientists dedicated to the future of Los Alamos, not all members of the newly-formed Atomic Energy Commission felt the same. On the Laboratory's 25th anniversary in 1968, AEC Chairman Glenn T. Seaborg commented: "I recall that when I joined the Commission's first General Advisory Committee as the most junior member of an otherwise illustrious group, Los Alamos was one of the first subjects of discussion.

Some of my colleagues maintained that it would never be possible to make Los Alamos attractive for competent scientists. It was too remote from civilization. The wartime buildings were already falling to pieces, and the cost of building permanent structures in such an isolated spot would be too costly. Furthermore, most of the 'big name' scientists had left Los Alamos with Oppenheimer. Those remaining might be competent young men with more than average ability, but they could hardly be compared to the giants of the war years. To be specific, some of the GAC members questioned the capabilities of the young Navy commander who had succeeded Oppenheimer as director. Norris Bradbury was an excellent physicist and had done an outstanding job on the Trinity test, but could he fill Oppenheimer's shoes? In early 1947 at least a substantial minority of the GAC believed that neither Los Alamos nor Norris Bradbury would long be on the atomic energy scene."

To second-guess what would have happened if the University of California had not renewed its contract to operate the Los Alamos Scientific Laboratory under the newly-formed Atomic Energy Commission, one might have seen the GAC minority's prediction come true. But Bradbury was aware of the forthcoming expiration of the contract and of how little contact he had with the University. "The contract was only a couple of pages long," he said "and I was aware of a gentleman in the business office named Al Dyhre who seemed to be in contact with the University. Dyhre worked for Bob Underhill. Underhill and I later became close friends.

"By 1947 I guess the University had decided that 'this Bradbury fellow' could be trusted or something because

I was asked to help negotiate the next contract. Underhill said something to the effect, 'Now look, you get busy and help us negotiate this contract. You've got to live with it.'"

Underhill, who had negotiated the first contract for operation of the Laboratory during the war, recently noted, "The contract which I negotiated and signed in 1943 had a clause whereby the University could terminate three months after cessation of war with the Axis powers, and the University served notice of termination since there

Contract with the University of California is renewed in 1948. Seated left to right: Carroll Tyler, Manager of AEC Area Office in Santa Fe; Robert Underhill, Board of Regents Secretary, University of California; standing: Ralph P. Johnson, Manager of the AEC Los Alamos Field Office, and Norris Bradbury. (LAHS photo)

was a serious question about operating outside California except under the necessities and liberalities due to war conditions. It also seemed inappropriate to operate a Laboratory with no close contact with the operation and no actual direction. But the withdrawal was canceled and I think this is where my acquaintance with Norris really started.

"After assurance the University would no longer be a 'mandatory' contractor and the operation would be subject to University general procedures, I met with Dr. Bradbury in his office in January of 1948 to review a contract draft. To say he was horrified is putting it mildly. The two-page document appointed the AEC manager in effect the prosecuting attorney, judge, jury, and executioner and the contractor in effect a slave. That started Norris as a contract negotiator and a great man on that team.

"At Eniwetok I sensed that Norris, like a Navy captain, ran a tight ship, and some members of the team did not voice disagreement. A man was in my room inappropriately expressing some disagreement when he heard someone greet Norris on his entrance to the building. The window was open, and my companion took a quick dive out and disappeared."

It was in the early 1950s after the Russians detonated their first nuclear device that Los Alamos was again immersed in an urgent program of developing a bomb— one more powerful than the atomic bomb. This was the hydrogen explosive which was successfully tested in 1952 at the Eniwetok Proving Ground. "Until the Russians detonated their bomb," Bradbury said, "the US was enjoying a lead, and to build the hydrogen bomb meant re-establishing that lead. We started to spend more money and we went on a six-day week for about a year and a half. At the time we didn't know how to build a thermonuclear device."

Bradbury said that the building of the H-bomb is the Laboratory's greatest achievement since Trinity. "Anyone who knows what a critical mass is can build a fission bomb. But, we didn't have anywhere near that degree of knowledge when we started the development of the H-bomb. Comparing the two is like comparing apples and oranges. Both were monumental achievements, but they were 10 years apart; they were started with different degrees of knowledge and from different points. Like the wheel, we take them for granted now."

Following the detonation of the first hydrogen device— nicknamed Mike—there were major Laboratory and community improvements. A new technical area was built, and in 1957, the security gates that closed Los Alamos to the outside were taken down. Los Alamos was an "open" city. "Nothing really changed as far as the director's civic responsibilities were concerned until Los Alamos became an incorporated county," Bradbury said. "Then almost anything the director had to do with the community—like housing—kind of went away.

"The AEC made the mistake of taking a vote of the population to decide whether they wanted the gate open or not. The population voted against it quite heavily. The people were afraid the women and kids wouldn't be safe on the streets at night and things like that. They liked the security the fence provided; the kids liked it and looked

A bridge spanning Los Alamos Canyon was built in the early 1950s. The canyon separates much of the technical area of the Laboratory from the city of Los Alamos. (LANL photo)

foward to the time when they could have a badge. The AEC opened the gate anyway. The only thing I remember that was highly amusing was that it had only been open a couple of days and we had our first major burglary. The people who voted against opening the gate were saying 'ha, ha, we told you so, we told you so.' They caught the burglar, and as I recall, it was an ex-security guard."

It was also during 1957 that the Russians were successful in launching their first "Sputnik" satellite. Bradbury explained what impact this had on the Laboratory. "It rescued the nuclear rocket program [Rover], although we didn't really have one. After the hydrogen device had been detonated, we were asked how small and with how big of a yield we could make them. We did some feasibility studies, looking at nuclear rocketry for surface to surface missiles, but it proved to be too doggoned expensive.

92

We put in at least a couple of years on it and we were just about ready to put it back on the shelf and forget it.

"To add something like the nuclear rocket program made a big change in Laboratory activities and it meant more money. At one time we were spending $40 million a year on the Rover program.

"The Meson Facility [LAMPF] is of comparable size to what the Rover program was and will be a wonderful thing for the Laboratory to have. The Meson Facility will increase our fundamental research. It also has applications for applied research and for medicine. I don't think there is any overall trend in the Laboratory toward either applied or basic research. What's obvious is a trend toward diversification. We have many more projects than we did 20 years ago. Many of them are quite small, and many more of them are unclassified. In that sense we're becoming more like a national laboratory. Weapons research, after reaching a certain level about five years ago, has more or less leveled off. It now represents a lesser percentage of the Laboratory's total work.

"In the long run, the question the Laboratory may have to face is, what happens and what responsibility to the country will it have if a complete test ban treaty is signed. For a few years there would probably be no difficult problem. But later would come the question, 'With no testing, what do we need a weapons laboratory for?' Things like Rover, the Sherwood program, and the Meson Facility are other ways to play a national nuclear role.

"Science rode high after the war—we could do no wrong. Now people think about other things. The post-war years may have been the golden age for science and scientists and we may or may not have deserved it. Now maybe we're in the iron age. We may not deserve that either. But, we still have it pretty damned good."

Bradbury has always seemed to have a "feel" for the needs and desires of the general public. It was through his direction that the Los Alamos Science Museum and Exhibit Hall was established. The museum has grown rapidly in both size and visitations since it was established. In 1969 nearly 80,000 people from throughout the United States and some foreign countries toured the facility. "We established it for public relations," he said. "The public didn't know what we were doing up here and we had a lot of stuff around that we could put into a show-

Raemer Schreiber, associate director, with Bradbury. (LANL photo)

case. It seemed like a nice thing to do and we could show the taxpayers what was going on at the Laboratory."

He has granted numerous personal interviews to members of the news media, probably more than usual just prior to the 25th anniversary of Trinity last July. On an occasion when the Public Relations department had been contacted for a statement on Trinity from the director, Bradbury was hailed in the corridor as he was rushing back to his office. "Fiddle-dee-dee," he said jokingly, "I hate to talk about bombs on a hot day." He paused briefly, and then rattled off a short statement. He waited while it was typed out. Then he looked at it and said, "Aw, we ought to do better than a sentence or two for them," and raced down the corridor with the sheet of paper in one hand, tickling the cement blocks with the index finger of his other. He returned later with a longer statement he had roughed out on his own typewriter.

Bradbury has been a "regular" at the annual Science Youth Days, when high school students from the southwestern part of the United States are invited to tour Laboratory facilities. He has told the assembly of students many times "If you don't find science to be fun, don't go into it; it's hard and the financial rewards aren't great." Although Bradbury occasionally wears a suit, he is usually neatly clad in a sport shirt and slacks. "We might as well be comfortable," he said. "Who are we trying to impress?"

No task is slighted by Bradbury and no one is given the "brushoff." Whether it is a Laboratory problem or a personal problem of one of his staff, he is always ready to listen.

The Laboratory grew up informally. Although many of its staff have doctorates, they are not referred to as "doctor" or by any title other than their names. Bradbury also frowns on frills and fringes as evidenced by the lack of air conditioning, drapes, ornate furnishings and other niceties in his own office. According to his wife, he is the same way at home. "I've asked Norris about such things as a dishwasher and a garbage disposal," she said, "but he always says, 'What do we need that for? We can do our dishes,' or 'What do we need that for? I can carry out the garbage.'"

"It's been fun," said Bradbury about being director of the Laboratory. "If it hadn't been fun, I wouldn't have stayed as long as I have. You get a kind of vicarious pleasure from the Laboratory's successes in Nevada or here at home. I felt good...there was a certain sense of achievement when the first 5-MeV beam was produced at LAMPF....Oh, I didn't do it, but I felt good about it when it happened. And then there are administrative problems you work your way through, and when you do, you feel a satisfying sense of accomplishment.

"Schreib [Raemer Schreiber] and I have kind of divvied up the business. We keep each other informed so that each of us knows enough about the other's business to function in the other's absence.

"The job used to be more fun than it is now. Back in the early days when you needed something you got it and there were no questions asked. Now things are becoming more departmentalized, there is more bureaucracy, and Washington thinks more about waste disposal, money, property control, audits, and things like that. You fight off all kinds of rules and inspections, but you don't get rid of the problem, you only delay it."

The finale of Bradbury's directorship was two days of ceremonies honoring him for his quarter century of service. It crescendoed to the presentation of the coveted Enrico Fermi Award. Probably no one (except Bradbury) was surprised to have heard that the LASL director was selected to receive the award, which consists of $25,000, a gold medal and a citation, for his contributions to the nation's atomic energy program have been many. Prior to the two-day event Bradbury had been honored with a resolution from the University of California regents at a special dinner.

Among the many awards and honors received by Bradbury is the Navy's Legion of Merit, which he received in 1945. He holds honorary doctor of science degrees from Pomona College and Case Institute of Technology and an honorary doctor of laws degree from the University of New Mexico. In 1960 he received a certificate of appreciation from the regents of the University of California "for the great contribution he has made in research and development in nuclear and thermonuclear science, and for the prestige he has brought to the Laboratory and the University." This presentation was made on the anniversary of Bradbury's 15th year as director of the Laboratory.

In 1964 he received the annual New Mexico Academy of Science Achievement Award and in April 1966, the Department of Defense Distinguished Public Service Medal. The DOD award was for "exceptionally meritorious civilian service to the Armed Forces and the United

States of America in a position of great responsibility as director, Los Alamos Scientific Laboratory....The outstanding international reputation of the Los Alamos Laboratory is directly attributable to his exceptional leadership. The United States is indebted to Dr. Bradbury and his Laboratory, to a very large degree, for our present nuclear capability."

In February of 1968, Bradbury received the Atomic Energy Commission citation during ceremonies observing the Laboratory's 25th anniversary. This citation is the highest award given by the AEC and is presented to private individuals and employees of AEC contractors who have made especially meritorious contributions to or have been clearly outstanding in the nuclear energy program.

Bradbury is a Fellow of the National Academy of Sciences, a Fellow of the American Physical Society, and a member of Phi Beta Kappa and Sigma Xi. He served as a member of the U.S. Air Force Scientific Advisory Board and on the Science Advisory Committee in the Office of Defense Mobilization from 1955 until 1957.

Bradbury has also been active in his community and state. He participated in organizing the first Cub Scout pack in Los Alamos and was a charter member of the town's YMCA. He was the first commanding officer of the US Naval Reserve Research Company 9-9 in Los Alamos (February 1, 1950-June 30, 1951). He retired from the Navy with the rank of captain in 1961. He has served as a trustee, president, and vice president of the Los Alamos County Board of Education. He is currently a member of the Board of Regents of the University of New Mexico. He has been a member of the Board of Regents of the

Museum of New Mexico and president of the New
Mexico Archaeological Society. He has been a member
of the Los Alamos Medical Center Advisory Board since
January of 1964. Until 1951, when he was appointed a
professor of physics at the University of California, Bradbury had been on leave as professor of physics at Stanford. He has been on leave from the University's Berkeley campus to conduct his work at Los Alamos.

Today [1970] the Laboratory, which survived the post-
war uncertainties under his direction, has more than 4,000
employees, a capital investment of more than $260 mil-
lion, and an annual operating budget of over $100 mil-
lion. Not only has Los Alamos continued to be one of the
nation's foremost nuclear weapons laboratories, but it
now engages in a wide range of other nuclear research.

Although a firm believer in this country's nuclear deter-
rent and a strong proponent of the 1963 Limited Nuclear
Test Ban Treaty, Bradbury perhaps best expressed the
feelings of the country when he closed his testimony
before the Senate hearings on the nuclear test ban treaty
by saying, "I myself, with considerable knowledge of
nuclear things, with some knowledge of their military
use, but with only a plain citizen's feelings about people
and nations and hopes and fears, would prefer to try to
follow the path of hope."

The proper word for Bradbury's leaving the Laboratory
is "resigned." "When a man says he's going to retire,
you immediately start thinking about a rocking chair," he
said. "I'm not ready for one. We're going to continue to
live here in Los Alamos. I don't know of anywhere else
I'd prefer to go. I have no plans to take a job somewhere

else. I'll probably devote more time to the University of New Mexico regents job, and we'll probably visit Mexico again."

Colleagues Remember
The Bradbury Era
1983

Richard D. Baker
George A. Cowan
Eugene Eyster
J. Carson Mark
Dr. William Oakes
Louis Rosen

Moderated by *Los Alamos Science*

In 1970, twenty-five years after he had assumed leadership of the Laboratory "for a period of six months," Norris Bradbury retired. Years later, in 1983, in an interview with Los Alamos Science, *six of Bradbury's colleagues share their memories of those years in which he was director. Here is a transcript of that meeting, with slight editorial changes, as it appeared on the Internet.*

Science: *Norris Bradbury took over as director of Los Alamos in October 1945. Would you describe what he faced at that time and what he accomplished?*

Louis Rosen: I can put it very succinctly. Oppenheimer was the founder of this Laboratory; Bradbury was its savior. After the war many of us had other job offers and many were leaving the Lab. I went to Norris to ask for advice. Norris is a low-key but very effective man. He did an excellent job of helping people decide whether to stay here which was, first of all, in the national interest, and second, perhaps in their own interest as well. This was Bradbury's forte. We tend to forget what management is all about. Management is a tool of leadership. Norris so used it for the country and the Lab.

J. Carson Mark: With the end of the war, a large number of people who had been important to the Lab's direction and effectiveness could scarcely wait to get back to the place where they really thought of themselves as still being. Most of the well-known scientists were in that group. Bradbury himself wasn't sure about the future of the Lab or his own future. He was on leave from the physics department at Stanford, and he had a house there that his wife liked. But he accepted the assignment of director for six months, just to give time to decide what was to be done. In addition, the people in the military-scientific group called the Special Engineer Detachment, who had been drafted out of college and graduate school, were very eager to get back and finish their education. So by the end of 1945 the staff of the Lab had fallen by some very large factor, two or perhaps three. It was short of the technical and scientific staff that it needed in order to carry on meaningful activity.

Lab Remains Important

Bradbury turned this process around. He felt that the Laboratory must continue since it was the only place in the country where nuclear weapons could be put together. This is not to say that Bradbury was anxious to use nuclear weapons. But he felt that since the country had put so much effort into these devices and since they were so important, it would be a wrong thing if Los Alamos should not remain capable of producing them. Very shortly it became clear that international agreements on control would not be reached, and it would be necessary for this country to continue nuclear weapons work.

J. Carson Mark, head of theoretical physics between 1947 and 1973; later a Laboratory consultant and member of the Nuclear Regulatory Commission's Advisory Committee on Reactor Safeguards. (LANL photo)

Remember that when Bradbury took over, even the assembly of weapons was a problem because some of the necessary people for that task had already left. The United States was telling the world that we have the atomic bomb, and if you will join us we will throw it open for international control. But the fact was that without this place we didn't have atomic bombs and couldn't acquire more. At the same time the production of fissile materials necessary for weapon production was going through a similar loss of necessary people. The production plants were new and had been run on an emergency basis during wartime. Because they needed all kinds of fixing, their output was slowed down. That was also a part of the picture at the time that Norris took over the Lab. When Louis said that Norris was the savior of the Lab, he meant just that.

Richard D. Baker: If Norris hadn't stayed, or someone like him, I think the Lab would have collapsed. He was so sincere about the need for this Laboratory that he was very convincing when he talked to people about not leaving. And I have always been impressed that he accomplished the task in so short a time. He didn't have much time to save the place, you know.

Mark: Yes. The Lab had been built for a very particular short-range purpose—to build an atomic weapon and bring the war to a close. Some of the buildings and some of the apparatus arrangements were totally temporary. They had to be put on a working basis or else they couldn't be used.

Science: *What did Bradbury do to get the Lab established on a stable plane?*

Mark: Until the Atomic Energy Commission was established in January 1947, General Groves was the authority, although even his status was unclear. The Manhattan

105

District was formed for wartime and its charter ran out when the war ended, but Groves felt that nuclear weapons development was essential.

As soon as Norris took over he wrote to Groves outlining a proposal for what the Lab should attempt to work on and get done in the coming period. That was the basis on which plans were made and activities were carried out. Almost immediately came up the prospect of a test operation at Bikini Atoll in the Pacific. Simply to get the people, the instruments, the material, and the devices out there, and to arrange for all that required a large fraction of the effort that was available.

Baker: We also have to remember the technical status of the whole business. We had done barely enough, both theoretically and technologically, to get two weapons built. Norris had to get people to do more work on the fission bomb; he was also talked to a great deal at that time about the thermonuclear weapon. Since he assumed that the Lab would go ahead and continue to develop atomic weapons, he knew that Los Alamos would have to continue to produce a few of the gadgets. But it worried him that Los Alamos was the only place in the country that could build an atomic device. For example, all the fissionable material sent from either Hanford or Oak Ridge had to be purified, changed from a salt to a metal, and then fabricated in order to make a weapon. And we were the only ones who knew how to do it. Norris wanted to get the routine production activities out of the Laboratory as rapidly as possible because there was so much work to be done with the materials part of the bomb. We knew very little about plutonium, and we knew very little about its alloys. He used to say that, as the theorists and the designers improved the atomic devices, we were going to require a lot more out of the plutonium and enriched uranium in terms of fabrication, verification of theory, the whole bit.

To show how Bradbury went about things, I want to read part of a letter that he wrote to the Atomic Energy Commission before the Commission officially took office. It was dated November 14, 1946:

Richard D. Baker, manager of materials research and development from 1946 to 1979 for many of the Lab's programs; directed weapons work between 1979 and 1981; later a Lab consultant. (LANL photo)

The problem of production of atomic weapons has been considered. It is believed that no immediate change can be made in extent of production now being carried out at Los Alamos. However, if the philosophy of maintaining Los Alamos as an atomic weapon research center is carried out, it is suggested that plans be made to remove as much as possible of the routine activity from this site. This has the additional

> advantage of disseminating the
> knowledge of necessary technique as
> well as decreasing the seriousness to the
> nation of a major accident or catastrophe
> at Los Alamos.

At that time Norris would say that, as soon as we could get the production out, he wanted to start a great deal of research, applied and basic, on the actinide elements. Soon after, he started that work, and it is still going on. Norris Bradbury, as Louis said, was a very low-key person. He would always qualify his statements about the future by saying, "Look, I don't know where we are going, but if it goes where I think it will go…" But when he spoke he was certainly convincing.

Mark: Bake, would you happen to remember when it was possible to build a device any place but here?

Baker: I guess it was at least five years after the end of the war. Hanford started to fabricate the plutonium parts for us earlier, but then we had to assemble them. We produced only the Trinity-type devices.

Operation Crossroads

George A. Cowan: As Carson mentioned before, in early '46 the Laboratory was committed to go overseas to do the military exercise known as Operation Crossroads, and it occupied the attention of a lot of people. So there was a great deal of ordered activity even as people were coming and going, leaving and returning, and so forth. Operation Crossroads was sponsored largely by the Navy and was intended to determine the vulnerability of naval vessels to nuclear weapons. It consisted of the detonation of two fission devices, one under the surface of Bikini Lagoon and the other dropped from an airplane. These tests, which took place in July 1946, resulted in some of the classic pictures of the boat perched on top of a bridal veil of water raised by the underwater explosion. I was there when that picture was taken; in fact, I was flying in a B-17 with the photographer. It was right before I left the Laboratory to return to graduate school. At that time there wasn't much question in my mind about whether the Laboratory would continue.

Baker: Bradbury was doing all this planning and recruiting, and at the same time he had you people over in the Pacific doing those tests. He didn't wait for anyone—a phenomenal man.

Mark: But why they didn't round up a bunch of Japanese ships and use those for the targets at Bikini, I'll never understand. Instead we took some good overage American ships over there and beat them up. We also had to send a large fraction of our scientific staff. Remember that the first bombs almost had to be put together by graduate scientists. For example, although I don't know that [George] Kistiakowsky was absolutely required in the tower at Trinity, he was there. The people who put those pieces together had to really understand what they were doing and why the piece did what it did. They had to be able to say, "It does fit; it's all right."

Baker: Or, "It fits well enough."

Operation Crossroads, July 1946, second shot in series (Baker); underwater explosion sank eight ships and caused irradiated water to wash over all the ships, making them uninhabitable. (LANL collection LAHS photo)

Permanent Community Begins

Mark: It was clear in '46 that these weapons, although made at Los Alamos, had to be converted into military equipment that could be handled by people trained to handle them, just as airplanes are flown by guys who know how to fly but don't know how to build a plane. That transition had to be gotten through as fast as possible.

In talking of the great uncertainty throughout the fall of '45 and the continuing period, we should mention that the future of the Lab had to some extent been resolved by the middle of '46 because the permanent community was already being built.

Eugene Eyster: When I was here at Los Alamos after the Crossroads operation, I remember Max Roy's showing me the first two Western Area houses and his saying, "Now look. We're really going forward—there is going to be a continuing Laboratory and there are even going to be places for people to live!"

The first permanent housing was built in Western Area, two- and three-bedroom single and duplex units. Housing was assigned according to size of family, salary, and length of time in Los Alamos. (LAHS photo)

Baker: We were also building DP West at that time. During the war all the fissionable material, especially the plutonium, was handled in D Building. It was decided about the time of Trinity that a new plutonium facility had to be built, but they didn't spend very long designing. As I recall, by the time Bradbury took over, McKee, the contractor, had started construction on the building without a contract. He bought the materials out of his own company's pocket until the government could start reimbursing him. That site was built in about a year to a year and a half, and it served very well for years and years. It may be true that the Laboratory was floundering as to what to do in '46, but Norris was not acting that way; he was just going ahead making plans to have an atomic weapons laboratory coupled with a lot of research in the areas of nuclear physics, reactors, actinides, and so on. Very far-sighted.

Rosen: One of the greatest things Norris had a lot to do with from very early on was planning the future of this Laboratory. If this Laboratory was going to serve its function in the application of science to national defense, it had to prepare the way for doing things not only immediately but ten years, twenty years, thirty years hence. The only way to prepare yourself in that context is to develop the knowledge base, and to do so you must never shortchange the resources available to those in the Laboratory who are dedicated in whole or in part to basic research. That vision more than anything else was important to Bradbury's success.

I remember very well that during the Bradbury years we did not wait for somebody in Washington to decide what we should do. We worried and thought and worked on what our program should be, this was presented to the AEC or whomever, and then we got back something that said, "You shall do such and such," which was in many cases exactly what we told them we would do.

Early Years with the AEC

Baker: Norris decided even before the Commission was formed what he thought the Laboratory should do, and when the Commission was formed, putting it bluntly, he sort of told them what the Lab would do.

Mark: For the first four or five years after the AEC took over, the people in Washington, both on the staff of the Commission and in Congress, knew so little about what the possibilities were, what the options might be, that they either asked for or accepted the planning or proposing that was developed here. They would say, "Please explain why you think such and such is a good thing to do." That was the frame of mind in Washington up until the mid '50s when a large staff, which had to think of something for itself to do, decided it had to direct things. Also, by the mid '50s people in Washington had become more familiar with the nuclear field. Most of them learned for the first time in August 1945 that there were nuclei in atoms and things like that.

Dr. William Oakes: We often forget that in the early days we really didn't know much about what was what. In the '30s when I was in college and Fermi was in Italy doing his first experiments, plutonium wasn't known. It wasn't discovered until 1940. Cyclotrons had just been built, and the interest in x-rays and alpha, beta, and gamma rays were all new things. We knew very little about isotopes.

All of these were things we would have studied anyway whether there was a war or not, but the investigations that went on in relation to the bomb accelerated the process.

Rosen: As these gentlemen are talking and reconstructing some of the flavor of the Bradbury years, one thing comes to my mind. Every year Norris testified before Congress, and one time he was asked by some character, "What have you done recently to save money, cut costs?" Norris said, "A Laboratory such as Los Alamos is not established to save money. It is established to spend money."

Baker: And they answered, "Yes, sir."

Rosen: That ended that conference. Isn't that a far cry from the way things are now? I should emphasize that Norris didn't make decisions alone. In trying to understand where this Laboratory should go, he involved the staff. There was direct coupling between him and each division leader in the Laboratory.

Louis Rosen joined the Manhattan Project in 1946 to work on basic nuclear physics and defense applications; founder of the Meson Physics Facility. (LAHS photo)

Baker: He even worked the group leaders.

Rosen: He thought he knew everything that was going on in the Laboratory. He wasn't always right. One thing that he understood very well was that this Laboratory must be prepared to solve problems, unknown problems, national problems, when and if they arise. He was always concerned with maintaining that capability, and that reasoning led him to diversify the Laboratory about halfway through his tenure as director.

Science: *Was there some thought that the Laboratory would be involved in peaceful uses of atomic energy?*

Baker: Bradbury was moving along, as Louis said, awfully fast. He was looking forward to having research in lots of areas. For example, in August of '46—believe it or not—there was a meeting held here entitled "Conference on Alloys for Breeders." He was already starting to think about using fissionable materials for reactors and getting us in on it.

Science: *Could we turn now to the problems to be solved in the design and testing of nuclear weapons?*

Cowan: When I left in the fall of '46 it was clear to me that the Laboratory's most immediate and important task was to design smaller fission weapons. I guess the plan for the Sandstone tests was already beginning to take shape in late '46, and those tests took place in the spring of '48. Remember that the Trinity-type devices were heavy and cumbersome and didn't really fit into the standard bomb bay. In fact, after a bomb was dropped, the plane would have to go back for repairs. Also the original devices were overdesigned. They were designed to work well on top of a tower at Alamogordo.

Sandstone Tests in 1948

Mark: Let's go back a bit. Certainly, by the end of 1945 we recognized a number of quite obvious, important, first-order facts. One was that the engineering of the weapon device had to be gone over and tremendously improved so these weapons didn't have to be actually assembled here. That didn't really require so much design or testing, but it required a great deal of work. That proceeded immediately. Second, we needed weapons whose nuclear parts were of a different pattern than those in the Trinity device. Some calculations and many estimates made during the war indicated that the Trinity device was a conservatively designed weapon and that, if things worked well, other designs could make better use of the fissile materials being produced at Hanford and at Oak Ridge. Enriched uranium from Oak Ridge had been used only in the terribly inefficient gun-assembly pattern at Hiroshima. Plutonium had been used only in the much more effective implosion assembly pattern. But what would be desirable when you had a stockpile of both materials, either in hand or in the course of becoming, was not determined. A small selection of the very straightforward obvious options in weapons design were tried out at the Sandstone tests in the spring of 1948. These tests gave highly satisfying results that led to essentially immediate plans to make changes in the kinds of weapons for the military stockpile. The Mark 4 was the device anticipated for the stockpile. It would contain standard components that could be made by mass-production methods and could be put together by assembly-line techniques, so the end of routine production at Los Alamos was in sight. And most important from the practical point of view, this new implosion weapon would utilize the ample supply of uranium-235 being produced at Oak Ridge.

Another consideration being looked at was the size of the device. It was perhaps more evident to us than to the people in the Department of Defense that it would be convenient to have weapons of smaller physical size so that they would not necessarily require taking the large B-29 up in the air. Most planes were too small to carry a Trinity-type device, so the possibility of size reduction was a very natural line of inquiry. However, I don't believe the

Sandstone, second series of tests in the Marshall Islands, 1948, intended to test improved design of nuclear weapons before adding them to the nation's stockpile. (LANL photo)

tests on that point were made as early as the Sandstone tests of 1948, but rather in the tests of '51 and '52.

I might add that the directions in which improvements could be made were easy to picture in '46 but very much harder to realize, particularly when every last piece had to be made here.

Science: *When did weapons first begin to be stockpiled?*

Mark: About the end of August 1945. To the extent that the production plants produced material, it was converted, as near as could be managed, into devices that could have been used, had there been the occasion. But, as I mentioned earlier, there was a large slump in production at the end of '45. Consequently, we were not making tens of weapons per month or anything of that kind. It was necessary to take two to Bikini Island for Operation Crossroads in the first half of '46, and at that time they were not a trivial fraction of the stockpile.

Oakes: One question that arose during my contact with the Air Force was how does an airplane drop a bomb and get out of the way without getting blown up. This was not a problem for the B-29s carrying the early bombs at 30,000 feet, but one wondered how fast a smaller bomber would have to go. This was a question that changed the size and types of bombs.

Science: *While we are on design and early testing, can you describe the effort required to do the Sandstone tests?*

Mark: We had only enough manpower and technical capability to run three tests. They required sending hundreds of people from the Lab out to islands in the Pacific for a couple of months, and some many dozens were there longer than that getting the place ready. Also, before doing other tests one wanted to see how these experiments went, because it was by no means assured how good the results would be. We needed to explore the options of reducing the amount of fissile material or reducing the amount of high explosive. Could one make bombs this small or not? Those were the kinds of things in people's minds in 1948.

Oakes: The 707 wasn't operating in those days, so a good number of people and all the equipment had to go by boat.

Cowan: Some of us went in C-54s, and that was no luxury. There were no seats in them, just canvas slings in which you could sit for the twenty-four hours it took to get out there.

Mark: When I went to the tests in '48, I went sort of first class compared to what Bill is reminding us of. Pan Am actually cancelled a flight on its transpacific route. That flight flew to Japan every day of the year except on this particular day, when it became a special flight to Kwajalein for government-connected people only. They even had female hostesses on that plane, and we had seats. When we landed at Kwajalein, the hostesses were welcomed by a guard of Marines who escorted them to a little hut and stood guard over them all night.

Russia Detonates Atomic Weapon

Science: *Let's move ahead now to August 1949 when the Russians detonated their first atomic weapon. That came as a surprise to President Truman and to many in Washington. Was it a surprise at Los Alamos?*

Mark: The fact of the Russian test was not a total surprise to people who had given it any thought. Sometime they were going to have one, and '49 was not spectacularly early or late.

Science: *Was the test announced or discovered?*

Mark: It was not announced by the Russians. The American monitoring planes flying between the mainland and Japan picked up radioactivity in the air, and samples from filter papers were brought back to Los Alamos for analysis. I am not sure whether any other place in the country could have handled the analysis.

Cowan: Not at that time. There were also samples from rainwater collected on the roof of the Naval Research Laboratory in Washington, which was set up to do some analyses, but not in the same sense that the filter samples were handled at Los Alamos.

Baker: There was a monitoring system at that time?

Cowan: It had just been put into effect, perhaps weeks before, through the Air Force.

Mark: Here at the Lab, Rod Spence, George, and their colleagues in radiochemical diagnostics went to work to assess what was in that radioactivity. They concluded that the products had been formed in an explosive event rather than in a production reactor over a long time.

Cowan: The ratios of short-lived fission products to long-lived fission products can provide absolutely definitive information as to whether the event that produced them was drawn out over days, weeks, months, or occurred instantaneously. In this case the ratios said very clearly that all of the fission products were made at the same moment, which is characteristic of an explosion and of nothing else.

Mark: Didn't it take quite a number of days to be really certain of that conclusion?

Cowan: Yes. There were also quite a number of days spent in Washington talking to panels set up to find out whether indeed this evaluation was correct. It was all top secret. I can recall going to Washington where I'd been told I would be picked

George A. Cowan worked on radio-chemical diagnostics for weapons; Senior Fellow of the Laboratory; member of the White House Science Council. (LANL photo)

up at the airport by an intelligence person. I wasn't told what he looked like, and I didn't know how he would find me. When I got off the plane, I saw somebody in a trench coat slouching against the wall, so I walked up to him and said, "Are you waiting for me?" And he said, "Are you Dr. Cowan?" I picked him out right away.

Mark: I recall that, after the panels were convinced, it took quite a number of days in Washington to persuade President Truman that there was no doubt what the Russians had done. So it was four weeks or a month after the event before he announced that the Russians had made a nuclear explosion. The Russians just sat on their hands and didn't say a word about it.

Work on a Hydrogen Bomb

The Russian test caused a number of people, most of them not at Los Alamos, to feel that the nation was now in peril and must make a strong and tremendously impressive response to the terrible misdeed of the Russians. Teller, Lawrence, Alvarez, Lewis Strauss, Senator MacMahon, and Air Force Secretary Finletter were among those who suggested we should go all out to build a thermonuclear bomb that would produce an enormously larger yield than had been achieved with fission bombs. A lot of debate followed, involving many people in Washington with many differences of opinion. Then in January 1950 the President announced we were going to proceed with work on nuclear weapons of all sorts, including the hydrogen bomb. He didn't say we were going to have a crash program to get the hydrogen bomb going, and the Lab had been working on the hydrogen bomb in a secret fashion quite persistently from 1946 on. So Truman's words didn't necessarily mean that we did anything much different from what we had been doing because we didn't really know how to make a gadget that would work as a hydrogen bomb. However, Truman's announcement was regarded as a great victory by those who had been advocating a crash program, and it was taken by the AEC to represent something of that sort. Immediate plans were made to increase the production of nuclear weapons material, and the Los Alamos staff went on a six-day week for the next two and a half years or so—until November 1952 when the Mike test demonstrated that a large thermonuclear explosion was possible.

Cowan: Incidentally, when the first Russian atomic weapon was tested, some people speculated that the

The Mike test in 1952 demonstrated that a large thermonuclear explosion was feasible. (LANL photo)

Russians produced their plutonium with a heavy-water reactor, or something other than a graphite reactor, and that this reactor, since it produces an excess of neutrons, might be producing the large amounts of tritium needed for one version of a thermonuclear device. That speculation proved to be incorrect. The first Russian reactor was in fact an orthodox graphite reactor. But the notion that it might have been a breeder and that the Russians might be well on their way toward developing a thermonuclear device had something to do with the urgency regarding our own thermonuclear program.

Mark: The fact that Klaus Fuchs had provided information to the Russians also became public within days of the announcement that the United States was going to go ahead with work on hydrogen bombs. The Fuchs business caused additional confusion in Washington. "What could he have told the Russians? No doubt whatever he told them accounts for the fact that the Russians have a bomb now instead of in 1985." Such speculations were of course a great deal of nonsense. In retrospect it is not clear that Fuchs's information really made a large difference in the progress to be expected of the Russians if they started off much as we did.

Science: *What work needed to be done to make a hydrogen bomb?*

Mark: Well, you might think that when people talked about the hydrogen bomb they had a drawing of a device that simply needed to be built and tested. But in 1950 we didn't have such a drawing because we didn't know how to initiate a large thermonuclear explosion. There were possibilities of small experiments to make sure that we could set off thermonuclear reactions and that we understood how they proceeded. An example of that was the Greenhouse George shot of May 1951. That was the famous shot about which Ernest Lawrence cheerfully handed Edward Teller five dollars after he had learned from Louis Rosen that it had worked. The George shot used a very large fission explosion to set off a small thermonuclear one. Those were the first thermonuclear fusion reactions to take place on Earth. Our goal, however, was to produce a very large thermonuclear explosion, and we didn't know how to do that. We were proceeding anyway, and people like Baker and Marshall Holloway had a tremendous materials job on their hands. They rounded up a considerable number of new industrial enterprises to help do the mechanical things that had to be done. American Car and Foundry had been making bomb cases for the blockbuster 10,000-pound high-explosive bombs. They were the only place in the country that had the tooling for pieces of metal of the size that we would need. The A. D. Little Company knew something about cryogenics on a laboratory scale and was asked to work on a monstrous piece of cryogenic engineering. If we were going to make a thermonuclear device, we would have to have tritium and liquid hydrogen or liuid deuterium, not in a Dewar in a lab but in a container on a tower where it could take part in a nuclear experiment. Although that work had been in progress here, it was possible to increase the attention on it. The Bureau of Standards, which had never attracted tremendously generous funding, was quickly given money to hurry up and complete construction on their cryogenic lab in Boulder that would liquefy hydrogen in massive amounts. We needed it here for testing apparatus, and we needed it for the ultimate purpose.

There were many other people involved too. The Cambridge Corporation was making equipment to get large amounts of hydrogen from Boulder to here and to the Pacific. I am not sure what the metallurgists had to do.

Baker: They had to do a lot of work on the materials for Dewars. They were always worried about plutonium's getting brittle and stuff like that.

Mark: Never before had the problem of plutonium behavior at liquid hydrogen temperatures been faced. And there were plenty of problems with plutonium even at room temperature. Lots of people got set to work thinking of what should be done if we were to go ahead with what we called Little Edward. That was never carried beyond the conceptual stage, but it certainly required us to do a tremendous number of things, all in a compressed time scale compared to the normal rate. I might also mention that in addition to the design work, which kept us sleepless at night and sleepless by day for a whole year, there were lots of political things happening related to Edward Teller and his campaign for a second lab.

Baker: Most of the workers didn't pay any attention to those matters.

Mark: Of course, they didn't happen very much here; they happened in the offices of the Secretary of the Air Force and Senator McMahon. To return to the technical story, on the theoretical side we tried to calculate how thermonuclear reactions might possibly proceed, taking into account this effect or that effect that had been ignored before. There were also gaps in what was known about the neutron and thermonuclear cross sections, and, while that study had never stopped, it could obviously be given more emphasis. And, perhaps as much as in anything, we were engaged in trying to acquire additional people who might be helpful in thinking through what was needed to make the device work.

Between January 1950 until the end of January of 1951, our work carried in mind a pattern of device that has often been referred to as the Classical Super. However, the prospects for its working were uncertain. Then in February or March 1951 the Teller-Ulam concept came in sight, and that immediately struck people as something that could be put together and would work. It was then that the whole point of the studies shifted. This was before the Greenhouse George shot. Greenhouse George had been planned and, in fact, preparations for it were under way out in the Pacific when the Teller-Ulam concept was invented. The new concept led to the big powwow in Princeton in June of 1951 at which the AEC and the GAC [General Advisory Committee] responded by saying, "Please tell us how quickly you can move on it." A year and a half before, the GAC had said, "We don't think you should start a crash program on the ideas you have now." They got overruled. But in June 1951 they said, "That's something on which a crash program is warranted. Go ahead," and, "What do you need?" It was from that point on that we went out and made this really monstrous experiment in the form of Mike, which weighed about 140,000 pounds not counting the cryostat, the liquefaction plant, and the other stuff attached to it. And indeed it was a great success from the point of view of working about as well as the calculations had indicated it might. Mike wasn't a weapon, but it brought in sight the feasibility of weapons in which a fission explosion sets off a large thermonuclear explosion. That has been the main line of work ever since, with tremendous variations to make the devices weigh less than 140,000 pounds and make them fit into missiles.

Cowan: During this period following the Russian test, we were also involved in an accelerated program for testing small fission devices, which, by the way, was done at the Nevada Test Site in 1951.

Science: *Why did we begin testing in the continental United States?*

Cowan: In order to do things faster and more convniently than overseas. This additional test site was justified by the urgency of having to do certain things preparatory to the overseas tests, and the work there contributed significantly, I think, to the success in '52 of the Mike device. I remember one partcular event in Nevada, whose name I can't recall, that demonstrated that certain aspects of the principles involved in the design of Mike were presumably correct.

Mark: A test in the Pacific had to be scheduled and planned for something like a year in advance. It required a construction crew of several thousand people going halfway around the world with all the sanitary and whatever facilities that were needed. It took a group from the Lab, some going by boat, some by plane, to get out there and unpack their equipment, to see if it was still working or had broken on the way out, to string the wires and put them up, and so on. In Nevada you didn't need anything

The control room at the Nevada Test Site; Raemer Schreiber, left, Rod Spence, and Bradbury. (LAHS photo)

1951 detonation at the Nevada Test Site. (LANL photo)

like the task force that was necessary with working outside the continental limits. In Nevada people could actually use hotel rooms in Las Vegas and go to work in the morning.

Eyster: Al Graves had an arrangement whereby he could leave Los Alamos in the morning and return in the evening and still spend a useful fraction of the day out in Nevada. He had to leave home in the dark, and one morning he arrived there with one black shoe and one brown shoe.

Rosen: Actually it was during the tests of 1951 and 1952 that Bradbury's policy of encouraging basic research paid off in large measure. Those tests brought to bear instruments that were developed not to do the tests but to do quite different things in fundamental nuclear physics, electronic and nonelectronic instruments for measuring neutron spectra.

Cowan: There were also new radiochemical detectors incorporated in Greenhouse George. They were first suggested by Dick Garwin, at that time a consultant and a summer student at the Laboratory. Those detectors have since been used routinely in weapons testing. They came out of the basic research program in nuclear physics and nuclear chemistry and are a highly important diagnostic technique.

Rosen: We could fill a book with examples of the symbiosis between basic and applied research just from the experiences here over the past forty years.

Mark: Louis and his colleagues had been attempting to measure cross sections for various nuclear reactions at the Los Alamos accelerators, and they had devised instruments to get the best recording of the neutron energies and fluxes involved in those experiments. In the Pacific we also wanted to measure the neutron flux and neutron energies, and we wanted those measurements as a function of time during the explosions. The problem was by no means the same as in the accelerator experiments but was closely related. Louis and his group took their equipment, which was delicately mounted on glass and tripods and stuff in the lab, and boxed it up in such a way that it could sit close to many kilotons of explosion and still record the data.

Baker: Electronics was in its infancy then, and it was a tremendous job to make those detectors work under those conditions.

Cowan: Detectors and the electronics for them developed very fast during that period. We were moving away from particle detection with the old Geiger-Muller tube to detection with sodium iodide crystals. That was an enormous advance. Then multichannel analyzers came along; the first crude ones were a tremendous step forward because we could easily separate particle counts into energy bins and quickly determine the spectrum. Many of these new instruments were homegrown. Every three months the situation seemed to change as a tremendous amount of new stuff was designed and tested. Of course a very important aspect of this work was that money was no object. We could afford whatever we were able to do.

Rosen: All that had to be decided was what did we need to measure. Then the resources for accomplishing the measurement were available without further question.

Cowan: And we worked furiously to get the job done. We were on a six-day week and Sunday was supposed to be the day off, but that wasn't the case either. Nor did people necessarily go home to sleep at night; people sometimes slept in their offices.

Mark: One improvement Louis didn't mention relates to the fact that for many years he maintained a corps of housewives working four hours a day ruining their eyes peering into microscopes to get the data he was anxious to see. The mechanization of that work was a tremendous breakthrough.

Early computer tecnhology at the Laboratory: the MANIAC. (LANL photo)

Rosen: These women did an enormous amount of important and demanding work. They were looking at nuclear particle patterns through microscopes. We were often able to hire a young lady because she had decided she just couldn't have any children, but after she worked for about a year—we helped with the fertility problem in Los Alamos.

Large-Scale Computing

Cowan: During this same period our need for large-scale electronic computing in connection with calculations for thermonuclear devices had an important stimulating effect on the development of computers. Many of the calculations in '51 were carried out elsewhere because of our limited computing facilities.

Mark: They were carried out on the UNIVAC at Philadelphia and the SEAC at Washington and the Western Bureau of Standards machine and I think the ENIAC also.

Cowan: When did our computing capability start to exceed that at other places in the country?

Mark: It was probably around '52. Our own MANIAC began to work then, and we were also getting a 701 from IBM. As soon as IBM made further improvements, we switched to those and our computing capability became impressive very rapidly. We acquired the first samples of two or three successive generations of IBM machines.

Cowan: We were the first customer for everything.

Mark: So a stream of salesmen from all the computing manufacturers began to beat a track to the door.

Klaus Fuchs

Science: *You mentioned that knowledge of Fuchs's betrayal came at just about the same time that we initiated the big push for the hydrogen bomb. What was the reaction of Los Alamos to that revelation?*

Baker: I had known Fuchs quite well because he and I lived in the Big House during the war. He certainly was a charming fellow. Boy, was I mad when I found out he was spying for the Russians! But I doubt if helped them by more than six months or so.

Klaus Fuchs, who worked in the Manhattan Project from 1943, much of the time at the Los Alamos Laboratory in the Theoretical Division. He was convicted of espionage in 1949. (LAHS photo)

Mark: Reading the biography of Kurchatov by Golovin, I got the impression that Fuchs's information didn't bring them a great deal of news. They had an idea of what we were doing and had already started their own work on a fission device before Fuchs came to Los Alamos. Remember Flerov's paper on the spontaneous fission rate of uranium-238 in 1940. That was a tremendous bit of work for that time because the number of spontaneous fissions in uranium-238 is really very low. He reported his work in the *Physical Review* and didn't get a rise out of any American physicist because we had all been told this work is secret. He then said, "Gee, the Americans didn't comment on this. That's the kind of thing they would have gotten very excited about six months ago. They must be working on something secret."

Baker: I always felt that Fuchs helped them to go directly to the implosion system for plutonium rather than worrying as we did about obtaining extremely pure plutonium for gun-type devices. Fuchs surely knew that plutonium-240 underwent spontaneous fission and fouled up the gun device. Don't forget how great a turmoil there was here when we discovered plutonium-240 in the Hanford plutonium. For some reason we didn't expect it. We were going gun-wise at that time.

Mark: My reference to Flerov's work is not totally irrelevant because the Russians were tremendously well prepared to spot spontaneous fission. If they could see it in uranium-238, they could certainly see it in plutonium-240.

Cowan: Flerov's colleague Petrzhak told me that in 1943, when the Germans were advancing against the Russians and Russia was fighting for its life, he was called back from the Russian-German front to Moscow to join Kurchatov's group. 1943 was after the first chain reaction at Stagg Field in Chicago, and I suppose that might have had something to do with setting up the Russian group at a time when the country was in great danger of falling to the Nazis.

Mark: That was before Fuchs was here. He didn't come until '44.

Science: *What were other impacts of Fuchs's betrayal?*

Eyster: After the discovery of what he had been up to, our relations with the British in the field of nuclear weapons were abruptly and pretty completely cut off for some time.

Mark: They were in the soup before that because of difficulties with the Quebec Agreement between Roosevelt and Churchill.

Eyster: Considerably later we went back to talking to the British, and it was fairly instructive to us in the explosives business to see the course that the British had taken in the intervening years. We were surprised to learn that, in the main, British developments were very similar to ours.

Science: *When did you go back to working with the British?*

Mark: '58.

Science: *Were there any changes in security regulations following the Fuchs affair?*

Mark: I don't remember any change. The security regulations that came in with the Atomic Energy Act of 1946 were in some respects troublesome because everybody on board had to be reinvestigated. A number of people were dropped who had previously been thought to be all right, but that happened quite independently of Fuchs. The McCarthy hearings, which raised the specter of the government's being full of spies, intensified the security work somewhat, but I don't think Fuchs's betrayal in itself had any effect.

Baker: But when it was first known what Fuchs had done, there was a lot of clatter about poor security, poor clearance procedures, on and on.

Cowan: We didn't independently investigate Fuchs. He came to us as a loyal citizen who had been cleared by the British for access to this kind of institution.

Baker: One of the criticisms was, "Why didn't we clear him too?"

Cowan: That would have required going to Great Britain and conducting a security investigation, and besides that he was a German émigré.

Mark: Remember, the wartime clearance procedure was totally different from the clearance procedure that came into effect in 1947. During the war a guy might have associated with anybody at all, but if someone decided he was all right, he was all right.

Cowan: The security clearance after that took into account your wife's politics, her family's politics, your friends' and family's politics. This emphasis increased as a result of the McCarthy era so that in effect you weren't innocent until proved guilty, but instead you were almost guilty until proved innocent. Some people were unjustly denied clearances at that time.

The facts suggest that there were no spies around in the early '50s in spite of McCarthyism-type comments to the contrary, or at least there was nobody at a high level with an open channel of communication to the Russians to pass on the Teller-Ulam idea. In developing their fission bomb, the Russians demonstrated their technical competence to do things in about the same length of time that we required, but they nevertheless took three times as long to do something equivalent to our first real thermonuclear test. It took us a year and a half after the Teller-Ulam concept to go to a test, and it took the Russians four and a half years from that time.

Mark: I don't entirely acccept your point, George. Their first thermonuclear device was six years after their first fission bomb; ours was seven.

Cowan: But Carson, the Russians paid enormous attention to the significance of our thermonuclear event. The Kurchatov biography says that he was in effect given a blank check. He didn't get it to develop the fission weapon, but after Mike went off he had the resources of Mother Russia at his disposal. And nine months later the Russians tested a thermonuclear device. That was a tour de force, but it didn't imply any covert information about the new concept.

Mark: It suggsts that information wasn't flowing, but, even if it had been, their development of a thermonuclear device would have required a longer time than ours. When we started toward Mike in '51, it took about a year and a half, but by that time we had tested fission devices in Nevada and in the Greenhouse tests that were important to the success of Mike. In other words, we had a great deal more experience with fission bombs than the Russians had at the start of the four and a half years or so it took them to develop something equivalent. I don't know how to compare the times. But I agree that there is no evidence that they were speeded up by exchange of information. If there is any place where information might have had that effect, it was in China. They took two and a half years from their first fission bomb to their first thermonuclear.

Laboratory at Livermore

Science: *During the summer of 1952, prior to the Mike shot, a second weapons laboratory was being formed at Livermore. Did Los Alamos feel competitive toward the second weapons laboratory?*

Cowan: It is hard to recall how tolerant our views were at that time. I recall collaboration much more vividly than I do the notion of competition, although competition probably existed right from the beginning. On the other hand, it seems clear to me in retrospect that it was appropriate to set up a second weapons laboratory. There was too much at stake for the nation to rely entirely on one laboratory.

Eyster: There has been over the years a great deal of collaboration. When Livermore first started, we made explosives for them because they had not yet gotten any local facilities going. In many areas in explosives we would have meetings and say, "You think this thing is very important, but we don't. So why don't you work on it and tell us what you are doing and vice versa." We used to send them slightly censored monthly reports, censored only in the sense that administrative and local things were cut. The Livermore people quickly got hung up and could only send formal laboratory reports. We said, "Oh, to hell with it; we'll send ours to you anyway." Sure, Livermore developed silly things, but you can't really fault the institution of marriage just because it doesn't always work.

Eugene D. Eyster came to Los Alamos from the US Naval Ordnance Laboratory; worked in LANL management in field of explosives from 1949 until 1970. (Family photo)

Cowan: I once asked Rabi [I. I.] about this, and he said he felt the relationship between the two labs was that of big brother and little brother. Little brother was the guy who always felt he was overlooked and unappreciated. Big brother was not aware of it. That stuck in my mind because it explained some of the things that were going on at that time.

Mark: There was no well-spelled-out arrangement on sharing work. It was necessary to know all of the same things whether you were working on a design that originated there or here. Sharing the work meant exchanging information either place might have, or both. For example, cross sections had been measured there and measured here, and the answers were different. Collaboration was necessary to find out which was the better measurement or how to reconcile the discrepancy. The same was true ultimately with respect to computing techniques. The competition that is sometimes referred to—and was real—occurred during the past dozen years when a number of new weapons were scheduled for stockpile and it had to be decided whether a warhead of the Los Alamos model or the Livermore model would be used.

But to return to George's statement that the country could make sense of two labs and maybe even had a requirement for two, it was nevertheless started in a rather unpleasant way. It grew out of rather unfair and vicious criticism of Los Alamos. From the moment Teller left here in October of 1951—or perhaps even before—there was behind-the-scenes fomenting for a second lab. For a time it was even threatened that the Air Force would set up a second lab in Chicago because that was where Edward was. The AEC had to head that off.

Baker: Frankly, the split almost happened before the war ended because there was so much dissatisfaction.

Mark: The timing was also questionable because in the summer of 1952 Los Alamos was strained to an incredible extent preparing for the tests coming on in November. But except for the unpleasant beginning, which has nothing to do with the Livermore people, the relationship was a good one.

McCarthy Hearings

Science: *As you mentioned earlier, McCarthyism was in full swing in the early 1950s. Did the McCarthy hearings affect the Los Alamos staff?*

Mark: They didn't bear very hard on individuals here, but they made everybody somewhat nervous and disgusted. But that atmosphere quite possibly had something to do with the fact of the Oppenheimer hearing. The administration, the AEC, the Secretary of State, and so forth, had word that McCarthy was showing interest in the Oppenheimer file. They felt that they had to prove somehow that this had been looked after and everything was all right before they turned it loose for a sideshow such as McCarthy was so fond of—not that they came off much better.

Science: *What was known about the Oppenheimer case at Los Alamos?*

Mark: Well, almost nothing was known, except the fact that he was under investigation, until after the public announcement that his clearance had been revoked. In December 1953 I had to go on an excursion to Washington, and, as usual, I planned to go by Princeton to talk to Johnny von Neumann. Norris, aware that I was going to

Norris Bradbury and J. Robert Oppenheimer, the first two directors of the Laboratory. (LANL photo)

Princeton, called me aside and said, "I am sorry to have to tell you that you shouldn't continue to discuss programs with Oppenheimer." That was the first word I had that there was anything under discussion at all. The hearings occurred in the spring of '54, and the AEC decided to lift his clearance about the end of June 1954, two days before Oppie's consultant contract ran out.

Science: *Had he been a frequent visitor to the Laboratory during this period?*

Mark: Not a very frequent but a very natural one. He had been chairman of the General Advisory Committee. Norris and others on the staff would appear before the GAC to tell them what we were doing. So he was very frequently in touch with the work, although he wasn't a terribly frequent visitor to the Laboratory.

Cowan: Why was Oppenheimer brought before a hearing?

Mark: It was at Oppenheimer's insistence. He was offered in December the opportunity to resign. He said he couldn't accept that because it would be resigning under a cloud, and he wanted to clear it up.

Science: *What was the response at Los Alamos when you heard the results of the hearing?*

Mark: There were certainly a number of people here and in other parts of the country who attached a very strong feeling to it. There was the famous event of Bob Christie's not shaking hands with Edward at breakfast at the Lodge here the day after he heard about the situation. There were people who wouldn't associate socially with Edward for years. There were a mixture of responses. It didn't affect the Lab's work; it did affect many personal relationships, but that's now thirty years ago and some of the bad feelings have been softened or been forgotten.

Cowan: There was no official response from the Lab, but a chapter of the Federation of Atomic Scientists at Los Alamos met and drafted written comments concerning the security procedures and practices of the Atomic Energy Commission. These were all inspired by the reaction to the Oppenheimer hearing. The comments were pretty caustic and highly critical, particularly of the guilt-by-association aspect. Lewis Strauss visited at that time, and an indignant group of scientists went to see him at the height of their indignation. He was so skillful in flattering everybody that he had us eating out of his hand in about ten minutes. As soon as he left, people turned to each other and said, "What happened?"

Nonweapon Research Projects

Science: *The Laboratory became involved in a number of nonweapon research projects during Bradbury's tenure. Can you describe how they got started?*

Mark: The fast reactor Clementine was approved in late '45 to investigate plutonium as a possible reactor fuel. It had never been used in a reactor, and the only place in the country, or for that matter in the world, that was prepared to handle plutonium was Los Alamos. Also, it was known then that a successful breeder process would most likely use plutonium as a fuel. After Clementine there were LAPRE and LAMPRE. These were also experimental plutonium reactors.

Baker: Most interesting to me was that the country, and particularly people at this Laboratory, started to think about using plutonium as a reactor fuel so early in the game. Programs that would generate knowledge on plutonium alloys and the like were set up with a view toward reactor fuels. So in addition to all the development work and intense effort on fission and thermonuclear weapons, there was other thinking going on in the Lab on research and reactors. To a great extent this was precipitated by Norris Bradbury's attitude toward research.

Mark: The plutonium reactor work doesn't deserve to be called a major nonweapon program. But it started very early and it took a lot of work. The country was going in all directions in reactors. Argonne Lab was thinking of two or three kinds, Clinton Lab was thinking of some others. Monsanto was thinking of a different one, and so on. The Air Force was thinking of going around the world in their nuclear plane, and there was no point to our getting into that business. If there was a point to our being in the reactor business, it was by the plutonium route. People wanted to do it because it would be related to weapon problems, but it never became a program to the extent that Project Sherwood did. Project Sherwood was the first research effort devoted to fusion. Jim Tuck was its main protagonist at the start and for some time after that. He thought that there was a way to get thermonuclear reactions to proceed in a controlled

Project Sherwood, a program designed to achieve magnetic fusion energy. (LANL photo)

way. So he set up experiments to explore this possibility and immediately perceived difficulties that neither he nor anybody else had ever thought of. Controlled fusion is still full of difficulties.

Science: *How was it funded?*

Mark: At first it was probably funded from general research funds because it didn't spend much money. But it soon became a serious, separately funded activity. And of course it grew up in other places in the country and so became an official AEC program.

Cowan: One of the major contributors to the theory of controlled thermonuclear reactions was Marshall Rosenbluth, who came to Los Alamos and worked on it rather early in the game.

Mark: One summer in the early '50s I had a really distinguished, tremendously capable bunch of consultants, and I thought how good it would be if they would work on weapons. Much to my disgust the whole crowd of them went off and worked instead on Sherwood.

Cowan: Project Sherwood was, in fact, the first major nonweapon program. Then in '55 we began work on a nuclear rocket—that was the Rover Project—and in '59 or thereabout we started UHTREX, the ultra-high temperature reactor experiment.

Health Physics

Mark: We are forgetting to mention an even earlier program that had to do with health physics.

Baker: We are. Norris Bradbury was very adamant on starting a health physics program and research on radiation effects.

Cowan: Much of it was concerned with the physiological problems produced by exposure to plutonium and tritium and then to fallout from nuclear explosions, fission-product fallout.

William R. Oakes, MD, came to Los Alamos in 1947 as chief of surgery at the medical center and consultant at the Laboratory; physician in Health Division between 1974 and 1981. (LANL photo)

Science: *Bill, you were part of the health physics effort. Can you describe some of what went on?*

Oakes: Yes. But first let me say how I came to be here. Louis Hempelmann, who headed the medical health program at Los Alamos, came to Washington University, where I was a physician, and talked to me about the exciting things that could be done at Los Alamos. Among them was the possibility of studying molecules and their metabolism by tagging them with radioactive carbon produced at Los Alamos. I had spent much of my career worrying about the problems of radioactive materials, and the idea of using these materials for research seemed to me to be one of the great new viewpoints. I had had quite enough of the military function during the war as a member of the Air Force, and the fact that Los Alamos was now under the civilian Atomic Energy Commission was an important factor in my deciding to come here.

Science: *What was known at that time about radiation hazards?*

Oakes: Physicians and people in general had learned from World War I that the handling of radium was a very dangerous thing. At that time watch-dial painters had become seriously ill from putting the brushes in their mouths. We knew that plutonium, being a heavy metal, deposited in the bones and caused destruction and eventual bone tumors. Plutonium is an alpha emitter and is not dangerous on the outside of your body, but if you breathe it in or swallow it you are probably in trouble. We knew that people who were exposed to plutonium and the other actinide elements should be protected. Hempelmann came to Los Alamos to get this job done. Special air-handling areas were set up where people worked with plutonium so that the plutonium would travel away from the worker in case of an accident. The nice thing during wartime was that the technicians handling plutonium knew the basic facts and thus understood the problems. Attempts were also made, primarily with film badges to determine whether or not people had been exposed to radiation.

Mark: And colonies of mice and even some expensive dogs were exposed to air containing plutonium and then studied.

Eyster: I can remember we devoted a lot of time on the first electron microscope to studying beryllium oxide samples.

Cowan: Yes. Beryllium was used in the atomic energy program. It was recognized shortly after the war that exposure to this element caused berylliosis, and that was one of the health concerns.

Baker: Louis Hempelmann was dedicated to protecting the staff and so was Norris. But they didn't frighten us. Health and safety were really sold to us, not imposed.

Mark: They had a lot of things to watch, and they knew what they were doing, at least qualitatively. They had a very good record of keeping bad things from happening to people.

Cowan: I can't resist mentioning some experiments to find out the rate of elimination of tritium from the body. These experiments involved inhaling a whiff of tritium gas and then setting up a diuresis by consuming so much beer per hour, free government beer. All the output was measured.

Rosen: I took part in those experiments and was one of those who got more tritium than was allowed at the time. My problem was that I didn't like beer.

Baker: Some have given the impression that when we started working with tritium, plutonium, and enriched uranium we just barged around without paying any attention to the health or safety aspects. That was just not true. Hemplemann convinced all the people working with the material to be careful, and so we all worked with him. We built enclosures for handling plutonium, they gave us nose counts, and we had monitoring instruments, which didn't go down to as low a level as one might want now but did tick if there were alphas around. It was pretty well handled and I think quite a plus for Louis Hempelmann. He didn't come around and try to scare anybody. He just told us we had to get off the dime.

Mark: I think he had a team with him who shared his ideas and made the effort effective.

Baker: We didn't take chances either in the processing or storage of materials. Everyone knew all about the dangers of accumulating critical masses.

Mark: Also the group of forty people or so who had more than the prescribed exposure to plutonium have been followed; Hempelmann is still involved in following that group. To summarize, health physics was a separate program. Although it was necessary in connection with weapons it really went into a much broader field.

Baker: Norris, even in the early days, did not limit what people did with so-called weapons money to just weapons problems. In the case of health physics, if it was related to radiation and the like, his attitude was "Fine, let's get on with it." Of course if there was something red-hot in weapons you had better do that first.

Cowan: An example, not of a program but of the scientific spin-offs, was in radiochemistry. Radiochemists had the freedom to investigate the debris from the Mike explosion, and the result was the discovery of two new elements, einsteinium and fermium, and of all the heavy isotopes of plutonium including plutonium-244, which was later found to exist in nature because it is so long-lived. In one very intensive period of activity following Mike, we extended what was known about the transplutonic elements by almost as much as what has been learned since. The neutron flux in that explosion was so intense that it produced everything up to mass 255. All of these products were identified and characterized. Previously there had been no way to make these things or even to know they existed. Later on, in '59, a symposium on scientific applications of nuclear explosions was held here. We discussed applications of nuclear explosions to basic scientific research that would in turn feed back into our diagnostic techniques, such as the use of neutrons from explosions for time-of-flight cross-section measurements. The effort to produce new heavy elements beyond einsteinium and fermium dated from that time and resulted in a spectacular improvement in the neutron flux produced in thermonuclear devices. However, it failed to produce new elements because of what might be called an accident of nuclear physics: the excess neutrons in the nucleus produce a catastrophic shortening of the lifetimes of the products due to spontaneous fission. They become so short-lived that there is no time to dig the products out of the ground and identify them after an explosion. We discovered that afterward. But at any rate the technical feats accomplished at that time—Livermore was also involved with these experiments—were really quite spectacular.

Science: *Did these efforts help weapons development?*

Cowan: It certainly helped to improve the diagnostic techniques. For example, the desire to identify a few atoms of new heavy elements in the radiochemical samples from an explosion inspired the acquisition of one of the first mass separators. Having been brought in to look for new heavy elements, it was very quickly pre-empted by the diagnostic people who found it so useful that they took it over full time. The people who were looking for heavy elements had to go off and negotiate for a second one.

Mark: The capability and experience with ion-exchange columns was also increased.

Cowan: Yes, I can still recall the decision to process a kilogram of dirt from Nevada at a time when people were used to processing gram amounts. Everyone involved rose to the occasion and found it was possible. Then there was no reason not to do all sorts of new things with diagnostic detectors that had never been thought of before. These new techniques became fairly standard. So the freedom at Los Alamos to pursue new ideas helped to stimulate all sorts of new technology. It led to excitement to intellectual challenges, and to all sorts of things that are very easy to lose in its absence.

Baker: Such an enlightened attitude was also very important to recruiting, whether we realized it or not.

The Rover Program

Science: *How did the Rover program get started?*

Cowan: I associate it with Bussard and the notion that the country needed an intercontinental ballistic missile for security purposes and that the only way it could be done was with nuclear power. Once Bussard introduced that idea, it excited a lot of interest. The reactor design involved passing hydrogen gas through a fission reactor core, thereby cooling the core and heating the hydrogen to the extremely high temperatures necessary to propel a rocket. The hydrogen thus served as the reactor moderator, coolant, and propellant.

Baker: Norris Bradbury thought the whole idea was interesting and simply started it up without separate funding. That's the way we used to work. We had to come up with a fuel that was compatible with very high temperatures and compatible with what the designers thought they could do relative to the size, weight, and power requirements of the reactor. We worked on two types of fuels. One was a uranium dioxide cermet, a fuel made by mixing uranium dioxide with a metal like molybdenum and forming it into a solid piece. The second was a mixture of uranium carbide and graphite formed by graphitizing a mixture of uranium dioxide, carbon, and a binder. Eventually we developed a graphite fuel consisting of coated particles of uranium carbide in a graphite matrix. These were made by mixing the particles with graphite and a resin. The mixture was extruded into the form of the fuel elements and graphitized at high temperature. The designers worked on reactor designs for both types of fuel. We worked for a fair time using Norris's money and then very rapidly acquired separate funding. We went right ahead and developed the reactor and both fuels, but then the cermet-fueled reactor, Dumbo, was turned over to Argonne. Then Westinghouse was brought in because it

was visualized that while we were doing the reactor testing, industry should get ready to do the flight testing and
start the production of reactors for space application.

Mark: Is it true that UHTREX was almost a spin-off
from the Rover work since techniques for living with
high temperatures had been developed for that project?

Baker: UHTREX was a direct spin-off, I always felt, in
idea and fuel. It used extruded graphite fuel elements that
retained fission products. And there were holes in them
for the gas to flow through. It had a gas scrubber and all
that; it was a pretty neat reactor.

Science: *What happened to UHTREX?*

Baker: Milt Shaw of the AEC was taken with fast
breeder reactors. He often said he didn't want to divert
money to UHTREX; he wanted it all to go to the breeder.
It was a shame that the UHTREX work was cut off.

Mark: I remember that the breeder was costing more
and more above expectation. In order to keep it going
Milt took money from many projects, not only from
UHTREX.

Science: *What problems did you have to solve in developing high-temperature fuel elements?*

Baker: A graphite-based fuel element was in existence when we began the Rover project. It consisted of
little pellets of graphite containing coated particles that
retained the fission products. The pellets were made by
molding and not by extrusion. For the Rover reactor we

wanted long fuel elements with holes for the hydrogen to pass through. But it was impossible to mold the many holes in these long fuel elements to very precise dimensions. We found a way to do it by extrusion. I always thought that was quite a technological feat. Another really terrific technological development was the coating of those holes with high-temperature carbides so you could buzz hydrogen through those fuel elements at something like 2000 degrees Centigrade without chewing them all up.

In the Bradbury years we also started a very vigorous program with Milt Shaw on uranium and plutonium carbide fuels for breeder reactors. That program has an old heart now and is barely breathing, but it survived Milt Shaw. And we worked for Argonne on uranium alloy fuels for fast reactors.

Mark: The Lab also built some of the fuel elements for the SNAP reactors; that work anticipated the work on heart pacers.

Baker: We got into the SNAP fuels under Norris. They were plutonium-238 fuels for space power sources. Then during the last year or two of Norris's stewardship, we developed plutonium-238 power sources for heart pacers. I want to say again that a lot of this work came because of Norris's attitude that we should look into whatever we thought we could do. Once we had looked into it, we would go to Washington and discuss it as a possible separate program, but we always had a fair amount of discretionary money to try out our bright ideas. I am not criticizing the present Laboratory administration because I know things are different now, but, gee, it was great.

Mark: There has also been a change in Washington. The present attitude goes something like this, "Here is the project you are to be working on; how much does it cost? A hundred thousand dollars? OK. When will it be finished? Tell us right now what the results are going to be!"

Baker: We went into that regime under Norris.

Mark: It began to move that way.

Eyster: I can remember very early in the game when the notion got around here that there ought to be some tactical weapons that were essentially free rockets, rockets without a lot of guidance. There was no one in the Army who felt this project truly came within their mission, so Norris convinced Captain Tyler, the AEC area manager, to engage in a ploy. I remember going with Norris and Tyler in the big Carco airplane out to the Naval Ordnance Test Station at Inyokern. It was arranged for the AEC to give them some money to work on a two-stage free rocket for tactical uses. Finally the Army heard about it; they got so mad that they did indeed develop Honest John, a single-stage free rocket. I think it just recently went out of service.

Cowan: This comment may be a little facetious but not entirely. We were done in by the development of large computers which permitted the identification and so the cost control of every so-called cost center down to $5000. In the '50s McNamara and his whiz kids came into the Department of Defense and brought in this revolutionary idea of controlling all that went on by setting up this accounting system. That spread like a malicious disease, and it has led to so-called micromanagement. It couldn't have been done without modern computer technology.

Science: *The weapons program was going strong in the late 1950s with the rapid development of more convenient versions of hydrogen bombs. Then in 1958 and 1959 the United States participated in the test ban conference, and in 1959 we agreed to a moratorium on testing. What was the impact of these events on the Laboratory?*

Cowan: I think it provided impetus to diversification of the Lab's programs.

Mark: A diverse program had already been built up at Los Alamos, but the moratorium added a strong talking point to the LAMPF project, which got itself recognized and put into gear along about '62 or '63. LAMPF was to be a linear accelerator that would serve as both a meson factory and an intense source of neutrons. It would interest a lot of the weapons people in case we got out of the testing business, and it had its own value as well. Diversification of the Lab meant that if a sudden test ban came on you wouldn't suddenly have to dismantle the whole Lab's budget and personnel.

Science: *What happened to testing after 1959?*

Mark: There was a moratorium during which no tests were done. Then they were resumed in '61 and '62. Then in '63 under the Limited Test Ban Treaty, tests were all to be conducted underground. We have had more tests underground than we ever had in the air.

Baker: Two other areas that Norris recognized from early on and that have since blossomed into large efforts at the Laboratory are waste disposal and the safeguarding of nuclear fuels. From the beginning we were working on safeguards, that is, systems that could detect gross diversions of nuclear materials. We were doing, to the best of our ability complete accountability, which is a safeguards buzz word for keeping track of where it all is. We were also doing neutron interrogation to measure these materials very early in the game.

Mark: The work on safeguards was partly promoted by Senator Hickenlooper's hearings on where those 4 grams of uranium went.

Cowan: We should point out another significant change in the weapons program that occurred after 1959. The emphasis changed from qualitative new concepts in weapons design to systems engineering because the delivery system had changed from airplanes to transcontinental missiles. There came to be an increasing emphasis on the engineering aspects of weapons, their weights, the way they were configured, the way they could fit into a certain geometry, and so forth. The present emphasis is on the application of the very large energy outputs and short pulses produced by nuclear weapons. If there is a challenging field associated with weapons today, it is the exploitation of these special features of nuclear explosions. Today the weapons business has a different set of emphases, a different set of talents, and in many respects a different set of people.

Mark: To a large extent the ingredients of weapons haven't changed that much, but the modes of application have forced a tremendous change in the way you approach the problem of drawing up a weapon. If it is to go into a Minuteman, that is where you start; if the weapon doesn't fit the delivery vehicle, it doesn't have any significance.

Eyster: I would say that there have been about three red-hot ideas or concepts in nuclear weapons development. These worked and were attractive because they were simple.

Cowan: There were some other red-hot ideas that haven't been successful but presumably could be. For example, if it were possible to initiate a thermonuclear explosion with nothing but high explosives, I think that would have had a militarily significant impact.

Mark: That idea has been pursued; it just turned out, like Sherwood, to be very sticky.

Baker: You have to understand the physics first on that one.

Mark: It's a materials problem, like all of our problems.

Science: *How do you view the direction of the Lab now, and where do you think it should go?*

Mark: The Laboratory has been responding with the techniques, capabilities, and support that it can find to a broadening range of important national problems, and

I imagine that direction will persist if it continues to be supported. However, the tremendous elaboration, growth, and detail of management by administrators in Washington is going to make progress along such lines much harder than it was during the times we have been speaking of here. Although you had to check with Norris before you spent anything important, if you aroused his conviction that something should be looked into, you could go out and do it. That is how most of the things we have talked about got started.

The Lab will have a dull future unless it can find a way to use the best scientists from here and outside to sort out those things that would be worthwhile trying, whether they are approved programs or not. These people must also have enough influence and authority to assure that the work be directed not by the Bureau of the Budget but rather by the ideas themselves. If these are good ideas, some of them will succeed. But to find out you have to spend some man-years of work and perhaps quite a few.

Science: *Does Los Alamos have a role in arms control?*

Cowan: I think it would have been rather remarkable if the place in which the nuclear weapons expertise resided had itself taken on the advocacy of suspension of nuclear weapons development. It might have been entirely admirable, but it is not to be expected and it wasn't the role in which we were cast. Therefore we have been the advocates of weapons development. When a description of our position is leveled at the Laboratory as an accusation, I would say that is totally unfair.

Eyster: Winston Churchill once said that he did not intend to preside over the dismemberment of the British Empire.

Cowan: To somebody who says with a sense of indignation that the Laboratory has gone to Washington and argued for the continuaton of weapons testing, I would respond, "So what else is new? That is the Los Alamos role."

Mark: Los Alamos doesn't properly have a role in arms control. It shouldn't perhaps argue against it, but you can't expect it to be a front-line proponent saying we should get rid of weapons.

Science: *Have we provided technological assistance for arms control?*

Mark: That we have. The Vela satellite program to detect nuclear explosions in space is one instance.

Cowan: We have also participated in seismological developments for the detection of weapons tests underground.

Baker: The Laboratory has always sent representatives and advisors to Geneva and to other arms-control conferences.

Mark: So if there ever is a complete test ban treaty, the Lab might still have a role in the monitoring. We could advise on what things to look out for and how those things could be detected.

Science: *The administration is encouraging industry to increase its effort in research and development of new technology. How does that affect the Laboratory?*

Cowan: Historically we have always interfaced very, very closely with academia. That is where we have looked for our top staff people, where we try to maintain our credentials, and where we get most of our consultants. But we haven't interfaced much with industry except through purchase requests and contracts. We have generally been the customer and they the supplier. In the present environment we are looking much harder at our interface with industry and identifying cadres of people in industry with whom we can have scientific exchanges comparable to those we have had with academia. This may very well pay off in terms of accelerated diffusion of ideas to the marketplace. It still is a hypothesis rather than a demonstrated fact, although there are individual instances one can point to. But my own feeling is that these scientific exchanges with industry will pay off and will become a much more significant aspect of the Laboratory's contributions to national programs.

Baker: Isn't the government making it somewhat easier to interface with industry?

Cowan: Yes. They are now permitting patent rights to revert to the individual laboratories rather than remain government property. So now, if we have a brilliant idea, industry may negotiate on the basis, for example, of an exclusive manufacturing right. Under the previous policy all our ideas were available in the general marketplace, and that ran contrary to all the rules of a commercial enterprise. A businessman does not enter a new field in which the same technology is available to everybody because he runs the risk of making an investment, advancing the technology, and then watching his competitor take it over because it is government property.

Eyster: Well, Bake, you and I surely have had a long-continuing business with industry that wasn't entirely on a purchase basis. We worked very closely with industry to improve the design of numerically controlled machining tools so they could achieve the precision required in weapons manufacturing.

Cowan: I suspect you can say similar things about our elationships with the computer industry, with IBM, Control Data, Cray, and so forth. These were interactive relationships.

Mark: They certainly were, because some of their machines were built with suggestions and information from us. We said, "This is what we would like you to do rather than that."

Eyster: Industry did not always appear in the role of consultant because it had another way of being paid—the expectation of business, or the purchase of other types of machines, and so on. Academia doesn't usually have such prospects.

Cowan: Let me modify what I said. This relationship with industry has existed but it is being much more intensely pursued.

Baker: We probably gave the people who manufactured induction heaters one of the biggest boosts in their business. We would buy their high-frequency induction heaters, and an electronics buff here would fiddle around with them and make them better. Then we would tell the manufacturers, and they would go back and incorporate the new features.

Cowan: Industry has picked up cell sorters and other sorts of interesting spin-offs. But now this business of technology transfer is becoming a more defined activity. We have a defined relationship with academia through, for example, our consultantships. I think there is something to be learned in pursuing somewhat the same kind of thing with industry.

Baker: There is a great deal to be learned with this deal on the patents. And if DOE lawyers weren't so plentiful, we could go faster with it. But the thing I still don't see is how we are going to completely overcome the problem of proprietary information. A couple of us approached the carbon companies about what they could tell us. They replied, "We're not going to tell you a hell of a lot of anything because what we have is proprietary information. Even though it gives us an edge over our competitors for only about two or three years, that's better than no edge. So run along."

Aerial view of early Los Alamos Meson Physics Facility. (LANL photo)

Vice President Hubert Humphrey visits LAMPF; shown with Bradbury and Louis Rosen (back to camera), founder of LAMPF. (LANL photo)

Bradbury meets with Vice President Lyndon Johnson.
(LANL photo)

Harold Agnew, shown here with Bradbury, was the third
director of the Laboratory, succeeding Bradbury in 1970.
(LANL photo)

167

*General Curtis LeMay, Al Graves, and Norris Bradbury
take time out for a lighter moment. (LANL photo)*

Bradbuty meets Admiral Hyman Rickover at the Los Alamos airport. (LANL photo)

Bradbury with Robert Bacher. (LANL photo)

169

The Bradburys were among the many Hill residents who quickly made friends with their neighbors at San Ildefonso Pueblo. (LAHS photo)

Movie Star Linda Darnell makes a surprise visit to Los Alamos in 1946. (LANL photo)

*Lois and Norris at an island party bringing the South
Pacific to the Hill. (LAHS photo)*

*Norris finds a new way to travel in Ceylon. (LANL
photo)*

171

Carroll L. Tyler, AEC Manager of the Santa Fe Area, turns the Los Alamos schools over to the county of Los Alamos as Bradbury, president of the school board, watches. (1952 LAHS photo)

*Young Commander
Bradbury of the US
Navy. (Family photo)*

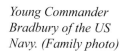

*Jim and his dad
attend a meeting of
Cub Scout Pack 22.
(LAHS photo)*

173

Norris with his first-born son, James Norris in 1935. (Family photo)

A few years later with Jim, right, and second son, John Platt. (Family photo)

David Edwin, shown here with the family dog, Nawa, was born in 1944 in Los Alamos. (Family photo)

The young family: Norris with Jimmy, Lois with John.
(Family photo)

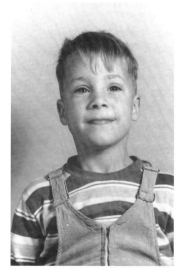

Mesa School Days for
David, 1950-51. (Family
photo)

Los Alamos High School
graduate David Bradbury, 1962.
(Family photo)

175

Jim and John in the early '40s. (Family photo)

John, David, and Jim with Nawa, about 1947. (Family photo)

*Norris and Lois entertaining in their home on the
occasion of their twenty-fifth wedding anniversary,
August 1958. (Family photo)*

Another twenty-five years saw them celebrating their fiftieth wedding anniversary in their garden, 1993. (Family photo)

Noted sculptor Glenna Goodacre created the bust of Norris Bradbury on display at the Bradbury Science Museum. Lois and Norris are shown here at the unveiling of the bust. Sig Hecker, fifth director of the Lab, is in the background. (Photo from Editor's collection)

Longtime friends and neigbors Norris and Lois Bradbury with Carson and Kay Mark, early '90s. (Family photo)

On the occasion of the unveiling and dedication of the bust of Norris Bradbury at the Bradbury Science Museum, June 9, 1993, Louis Rosen made the following statement:

> The time was 27 years ago. J. Robert Oppenheimer was visiting Los Alamos to present a lecture....There was a pre-lecture cocktail party at our home, and while Oppie was sipping a dry martini, I asked him, ever so delicately, how he was able to fathom that the very young Norris Bradbury would embody the technical, political, administrative and personal skills and courage that would enable him to halt the decline of the Los Alamos Laboratory and rebuild it into a world-class scientific institution. He replied that he had grave doubts whether Los Alamos could continue after the war, as a great scientific laboratory, but he felt that if anyone could make that happen, Bradbury could. Norris made it happen.

Oppenheimer's last visit to Los Alamos, 1963.

The Final Years

1970-1997

*A*n overflow crowd came to Trinity on the Hill
Episcopal Church for the funeral of Norris Bradbury on August 23, 1997. After the funeral and a
reception in the church parish hall, the family and a few
others—Lois, their sons with their wives, grandchildren,
faithful Fabie who had served Norris and Lois for twenty-
six years, some friends—retired to the Bradbury home.
A driving August storm had begun—thunder, lightning,
winds, and sheets of rain.

As the storm raged, and the survivors mourned and
remembered, suddenly lightning flashed through the sky,
striking an enormous pine in the backyard. The giant
tree exploded, scattering its debris over a wide area of
the yard and house. They watched in stunned silence.
Jim Bradbury said later that it seemed as if Norris were
reminding them not to be complacent, not to grieve too
long, but to take an interest in life and get on with it.

Now, several days later, the tolling of the great bell from
Fuller Lodge's belfry broke the silence of the August
afternoon as friends and family left the Lodge quietly at
the end of the memorial service. Burial had taken place at
Guaje Pines. This was the last formal celebration of the
life of Norris Bradbury. Mister Los Alamos was dead.

Bradbury's six-months promise to Oppenheimer had
extended to twenty-five years, the third quarter of the
twentieth century. He had guided the Lab's growth, after
the war and after many scientists and military personnel
had left the Hill, from a small staff of about twelve hundred to more than four thousand in 1970. He had seen the
single-purpose crash program to end the war expanded

to include a broad range of research on such projects as nuclear energy for peaceful uses, magnetic fusion, nuclear rocket propulsion, health applications, and many other projects related to basic research.

And he had watched—and helped—a small, neat city arise from the mud-covered roads and temporary buildings that barely supported the needs of wartime Los Alamos.

In 1946 Congress established the Atomic Energy Commission, a civilian body to replace military oversight of the Manhattan Project. Although Washington would continue its close contact with the Laboratory, it sought to remove itself from operating the town as soon as possible, and Los Alamos citizens were eager to run things themselves. In 1949 the AEC-controlled federal district of Los Alamos, which had been geographically a tiny part of Sandoval County, became the thirty-second county in the state of New Mexico.

In 1952 the AEC assigned the schools to Los Alamos County, though an AEC subsidy to the schools continued for many years. In 1957 some acreage was developed to provide land for privately owned homes, and by 1965 full-fledged disposal of government-owned housing was under way. Schools, churches, civic buildings, businesses, sports facilities all were sold to individuals or organizations, relieving the AEC of its position of landlord.

Architect of the Lab…Savior of the Lab…Father of the US nuclear arsenal. These titles he wore appropriately during the twenty-five years of his LASL leadership.

186

When he retired in 1970, Norris Bradbury was sixty-one years old and would live another twenty-seven years, most of them in active service to the town, to his church, to his family and friends, and to various government or business-related interests.

Governor David Cargo appointed him to the University of New Mexico Board of Regents in 1969, a time of unrest on university campuses across the country. In the spring of 1970, charges of censorship and interference with academic freedom provoked student demonstrations and strikes at UNM and finally forceful occupation of the Student Union Building by militants. Tensions mounted to the point that the National Guard was called in to restore order, and a number of students were wounded by bayonets of the guardsmen before a shaky peace was restored. In Santa Fe the legislature and the new governor, Bruce King, sought a more permanent solution, and in early 1971 Governor King replaced two of the regents, Norris Bradbury one of them.

Throughout most of the 1970s and into the 1980s Bradbury served on the local Episcopal parish vestry, once as senior warden, twice as junior warden. The responsibility of the junior warden is the general physical oversight of the building and grounds, often in a particularly hands-on style, so it is no accident that Bradbury was chosen to fill this position. He pulled weeds and tended flowers in the summer and shoveled snow in the winter. There is a story, perhaps apocryphal but credible, that a friend needed to see Norris and discovered when he called the Bradbury home that he could be reached at the church. The friend decided to drive to the church and speak to

Norris in person. Neither the rector nor the church secretary could help him locate the elusive junior warden. "Look around," he was told, "he is here somewhere." When the friend went into the parish hall, the first thing he saw was a pair of khaki-clad legs sticking out from under the kitchen sink. Norris had discovered a leak and was—of course—fixing it.

Harold Agnew, Bradbury's immediate successor at the Laboratory, invited him to serve as a senior consultant to LANL, but he chose not to accept. He did serve as a consultant, however, to various government agencies, working especially for the National Academy of Sciences, a job requiring frequent trips to Washington, DC. He also served as a member of the boards of the Los Alamos Medical Center, the First National Bank of Santa Fe, the Los Alamos YMCA, and the Santa Fe Neurological Society. He had even been parade marshall to the big annual summer parade in Los Alamos. He continued a vital interest in these and other organizations he had helped to found and to flourish.

He was often enlisted as informal consultant and friend to people in town; this task he always accepted happily. He had been president of the school board when the AEC transferred its ownership of the schools to Los Alamos County. He was often in later years a counselor to superintendent and teachers.

He had begun very early to implement a plan of cooperation between the Laboratory and area colleges and universities. As early as 1946 he called representatives of seventeen western institutions of higher learning to a conference dedicated to studying and implementing a plan for training students in scientific fields at the Laboratory, and his interest in furthering education never faltered from those early Los Alamos days.

Many years later, long after he had left the Laboratory, two young scientists, new Laboratory employees, had an opportunity to speak with Bradbury informally—where did he think science would head, especially in the environmental field relating to research and development needed on various topics. Said one of the young men, "His answer was one of the profound moments of my career, and his words both haunt me and inspire me: 'You guys are the ones who have to define this, then delineate [the science] that you want to do, then drop all pretense and go sell it to Congress. It won't happen any other way, and if you don't sell your ideas, someone else will grab the money.'"

At home he kept his garden healthy and productive, both flowers and vegetables, and he worked in his shop, crafting fine furniture, including a bed for each of his grandchildren, benches, gifts of woodwork.

David remembers Norris's arrival in Los Angeles, while David was attending UCLA, in the old Chevy pickup, the back piled high with handmade bedroom furniture carefully crafted, packed, and delivered for David's two daughters.

The '70s and '80s were times of travel for the Bradburys. During his years at the Laboratory Norris had spent a great deal of time traveling—to Washington, to the Pacific, to the Nevada Test Site—while Lois had stayed at home, caring for the boys and teaching music at Mesa School. Now it was time for them to travel together, and they made the most of it, going to places like Hong Kong, Ceylon, India, Kathmandu, the West Irian Islands, Scandinavia, various African countries, Australia, and others. And when Lois was tired of traveling, Norris could always find a son or two as companions on the journey. Jim and David recall their last trip with their father in about 1995 when they went deep into Mexico, Norris's favorite site.

Norris and Lois took great pleasure in their family, their sons and grandchildren. Jim's daughters, Kristen and Elise, grew up in Los Alamos. John's children, Wymond and Katie, lived for a short time with their grandparents as young children but spent most of their growing years in Colorado. Elizabeth and Andrea, David and Gloria's daughters, spent their childhood mostly in Tucson and Santa Fe.

Two of the Bradbury sons, Jim and David, worked at LANL, both now retired from the Lab. Jim works now with non-profit organizations involving the reduction of greenhouse gas emissions, using geographic information systems to assist vulnerable populations, and nuclear non-proliferation initiatives. John retired after many years service with the US Geological Survey and moved with his wife Vera to the mountains of southern Colorado just months before his untimely death in August 2005. The sons stayed close to Norris and Lois, frequently visiting and calling, often taking them on drives around the countryside and finding different places to take them for dinner once or twice a week.

*The last years were physically painful ones. Sometime in
the middle of the '90s Norris hit his leg with an axe while
chopping firewood. The wound became a non-healing
ulcer that he attempted to ignore until Lois persuaded
him to see a physician, but by that time it was too late to
prevent the invasion of infection that resisted all treatment and ultimately led to gangrene and to the amputation of his right leg just below the knee. Sometime later
when the infection had spread to the other leg, it was rec-
ommended that he have it also amputated. He and Lois
decided against this full amputation, however, but physicians removed several toes and a part of his foot. He took
to his wheel chair with grace, never complaining.*

*Fabie—Fabiola C de Baca—was the Bradburys' faith-
ful and devoted caretaker and helper who had come to
work for them in 1972. At first she came from her home in
Chimayó once a week, but as the years passed and their
needs grew greater, she spent more and more time with
Norris and Lois.*

*Almost every day Fabie pushed Norris around the neigh-
borhood. She said that as they went along he would frequently say, "Hold on!" She would stop, and he would
lean down as far as he could from his wheel chair to
pull two or three weeds he'd spotted. Then he'd say, "All
right. The rest can wait till tomorrow. Let's get on with
it." And they would continue their journey.*

*Lois and Norris grew even closer together as the years
passed. "They were just like a pair of lovebirds," Fabie
said. "Norris was always right beside Lois." Lois, who
had also developed painful ulcers on her legs and walked
with difficulty, loved to sit mornings on her special stool*

by the stove in her sunny kitchen, her crossword puzzle from the newspaper and her orange juice from breakfast on the counter beside her. Often visitors sat facing her on the bench Norris had made to fit especially in a spot in the kitchen. As Lois sat on her corner stool, or as she prepared food, Norris wheeled his chair nearby and sat, contentedly, as they made easy conversation or simply were there together.

Norris never gave up his role as kitchen helper. Usually after dinner Fabie washed the dishes and Norris dried, carefully placing the silverware in its proper place, trying to reach, but being not quite able to, the shelves for the dishes. Lois liked to watch early evening programs on public television, and Fabie and Norris went to another set where they often watched Spanish programs. Once, Fabie said, she switched to a baseball game. As Norris watched the young runner sprint around the bases, he said, "I wish I could run like that." This may have been the only near-complaint Fabie ever heard from him.

Another evening routine in the last years was music before bedtime, Lois playing her beloved piano, Norris in his wheel chair nearby. She loved Bach above all, but she also enjoyed hymns and other classic "oldies," many of which she played skillfully by ear. Fabie remembers that sometimes Norris would ask Lois to play his favorite, "You Are My Sunshine," and that would close the evening musicale.

In the last years his memory became faulty, but his family and friends remember that his interest in people and events stayed strong, that his smile and good humor were always with him. Even in the final days Norris wanted to be up and dressed and spending time with Lois and the friends who visited frequently.

The disease that had claimed his legs continued to ravish his body—and eventually also Lois's—until at last it won the battle. Late in the afternoon of August 20, with Lois and his sons nearby, Norris Bradbury died, a life well lived, a peaceful death well earned.

vne

Bibliography

There are scores of books and articles concerning the Laboratory at Los Alamos and the role of Norris Bradbury. The few listed below hold specific information of interest to this book.

Chambers, Marjorie Bell. *The Battle for Civil Rights or How Los Alamos Became a County.* Los Alamos Historical Society, 1999.

Christman, Al. *Target Hiroshima: Deak Parsons and the Creation of the Atomic Bomb.* Annapolis: Naval Institute Press, 1998.

Groves, General Leslie M. *Now It Can Be Told: The Story of the Manhattan Project.* Cambridge: Da Capo Press, 1962.

Horn, Calvin. *The University in Turmoil and Transition; Crisis Decades at the University of New Mexico.* Albuquerque: Rocky Mountain Publishing Co., 1981.

LASL News, January 1, 1963. "The First Twenty Years."

Martin, Craig. *Quads, Shoeboxes and Sunken Living Rooms: A History of Los Alamos Housing.* Los Alamos Historical Society, 2000.

McMillan, Priscilla J. *The Ruin of J. Robert Oppenheimer and the Birth of the Modern Arms Race.* New York: Viking Penguin Group, 2005.

Rhodes, Richard. *The Making of the Atomic Bomb.* New York: Simon and Schuster, 1986.

Shepley, James R. and Clay Blair, Jr. *The Hydrogen Bomb: The Men, the Menace, the Mechanism.* New York: David McKay Company, 1954.

Storms, Barbara. "Reach to the Unknown: The Trinity Story July 16, 1945," *The Atom*, Vol. 2, No. 8, Los Alamos Scientific Laboratory, July 16, 1965.

Thomson, David. *A Guide to the Nuclear Arms Control Treaties.* Los Alamos Historical Society, 2001.

Truslow, Edith. *Manhattan District History: Nonscientific Aspects of Los Alamos Project Y 1942 through 1946.* Los Alamos Scientific Laboratory, 1946. (Reprinted by Los Alamos Historical Society, 1997.)

Glossary of Names

Alvarez, Luis. (1911-1988) Professor in Radiation Lab at the University of California, Berkeley; Metallurgical Lab at the University of Chicago; LASL 1944-45; developed detonators for setting off the plutonium bomb; scientific observer at Trinity and Hiroshima.

Agnew, Harold. (b. 1921) Director of LANL from 1970 to 1979, Bradbury's immediate successor; received in 2001 LANL's first Los Alamos Medal, highest honor given by the Laboratory.

Anderson, Senator Clinton P. (1895-1973) Democratic senator from New Mexico 1949-1973; chairman of Joint Committee on Atomic Energy in 84th and 86th Congresses.

Bacher, Robert. (1905-2004) Leader of G (for *Gadget*) Division; responsible for design of implosion bomb (*Fat Man*).

Baker, Richard D. (1913-1985) Joined Manhattan Project in 1943 to work on metallurgy of plutonium and uranium; managed materials research and development for most of the Laboratory programs between 1946 and 1979; directed Laboratory weapons work between 1979 and 1981.

Breit, Gregory. (1899-1981) Coordinator of the Fast Neutron Project at the University of Chicago.

Bussard, Robert W. (b. 1928) His proposal that the key to nuclear rocket development was temperature-resistant materials convinced the Air Force and the AEC to set up a joint program at LASL to develop Rover, a nuclear rocket intended to be launched from the ground.

Cowan, George A. (b. 1920) Came to LASL for a short time in 1946; participated in Operation Crossroads; returned in 1949 to work on radiochemical diagnostics for weapons; associate head of the Laboratory Test Division as well as associate director for research activities; Senior Fellow of LANL.

Dyhre, Al E. (1898-1984) Purchasing agent for the Project, fiscal representative of the University of California, and business manager of the Laboratory.

Eisenhower, Dwight D. (1890-1969) US President 1953-1961; initiated negotiations for Limited Nuclear Test Ban Treaty.

Eyster, Eugene. (b. 1914) Came to LASL from US Naval Ordnance Laboratory in 1949; head of GX Division until 1970.

Fermi, Enrico. (1901-1954) Italian-born physicist; his work led to the first sustained nuclear chain reaction in Chicago in 1942; important scientist in Manhattan Project; became American citizen in 1944.

Feynman, Richard. (1918-1988) Group leader in Theoretical Division 1943-1945; with Hans Bethe devised formula for predicting energy yield of nuclear explosions.

Finletter, Thomas Knight. (1893-1980) Second Secretary of US Air Force 1950-1953; served under President Truman as chairman of Air Policy Commission.

Flerov, G. N. (1913-1990) Chairman of Scientific Council, USSR Academy of Sciences; founder and director of Flerov Laboratory of Nuclear Reactions; important work with Petrzhak.

Foster, John. (b. 1922) Designed fission bomb at Livermore; director of Lawrence Livermore National Laboratory 1961-1965.

Fuchs, Klaus. (1911-1988) Born in Germany; fled to England; interned briefly in 1940; when released, began work on British Tube Alloys (UK atomic bomb project); came to Los Alamos in 1943; passed secrets to USSR.

Garwin, Richard. (b. 1928) Came to LASL as consultant with Fermi in 1950; worked on new techniques for testing and diagnostics of the function of nuclear weapon designs and on the specific design of Mike.

Goldwater, Senator Barry. (1909-1998) Conservative Republican senator from Arizona 1953-1965, 1969-1987; candidate for President in 1964.

Golovin, Igor. Deputy and biographer of Kurchatov; reported that first Soviet atom bomb was based on drawing of the American bomb provided by spies.

Graves, Alvin C. (1909-1965) Leader of J Division; present at Stagg Field when first nuclear reactor went critical; present at criticality accident that killed Louis Slotin; test group leader for Ranger tests in 1951; scientific advisor for test managers.

Groves, General Leslie R. (1896-1970) Commissioned in 1918 to Army Corps of Engineers; oversaw construction of Pentagon, later in charge of Manhattan Project.

Hecker, Siegfried S. (b. 1943) Director of LANL from 1985 until 1997.

Hempelmann, Dr. Louis. (1914-1993) Invited by Oppenheimer to oversee health, safety, and radiation protection; studied effects of radiation, including radioisotopes in humans.

Hickenlooper, Senator Bourke B. (1896-1971) Conservative Republican senator from Iowa 1945-1969; chairman of Joint Committee on Atomic Energy (1949-52).

Holloway, Marshall. (d. 1991) Invited to join Manhattan Project by Oppenheimer in 1943; designed nuclear components for Fat Man; with Philip Morrison had overall responsibility for assembling plutonim core for Trinity test; in charge of Mike test.

Humphrey, Hubert. (1911-1978) Vice President under President Lyndon Baines Johnson.

Jette, Eric. (1897-1963) Group leader, then leader of CMR division after the war.

Johnson, Lyndon Baines. (1908-1973) Vice President under President John F. Kennedy; President from 1963 until 1969.

Johnson, Ralph P. Manager of AEC's Los Alamos Field Office.

Kellogg, J. M. B. (Jerry). (1905-1981) Head of Physics Division from 1946 until 1962.

Kennedy, John F. (1917-1963) US President 1961-1963, signed Limited Nuclear Test Ban Treaty, 1963.

King, Governor Bruce. (b. 1924) Three-time governor of New Mexico, 1971-1975, 1979-1983, and 1991-1995; responsible for replacing Bradbury on UNM Board of Regents.

King, Admiral Ernest. (1878-1956) Commander-in-Chief of the US Fleet.

Kistiakowsky, George. (1900-1982) Born in Russia, fled to Germany, joined Manhattan Project in 1944; became head of implosion department; under his leadership came the complex explosive lenses necessary to achieve critical mass.

Khrushchev, Nikita. (1894-1971) Leader of USSR, succeeding Josef Stalin, from 1955 until his death.

Kurchatov, I. V. (1903-1960) Leader of the Soviet atomic bomb project; his team built first USSR cyclotron; First Lightning, plutonium implosion bomb, detonated in 1949.

Lawrence, E. O. (1901-1958) Inventor of the cyclotron; director of Radiation Laboratory at University of California, later Lawrence Livermore National Laboratory.

LeMay, General Curtis E. (1906-1990) After World War II reorganized the Strategic Air Command into an effective means of conducting nuclear war.

Loeb, Leonard B. (1891-1978) Professor of physics at University of California, Berkeley.

MacDougall, Duncan. (1909-1990) Assistant director, Weapons Division at Los Alamos; undergraduate fraternity friend of Bradbury.

Manley, John. (1907-1990) Came to Los Alamos in 1943; became executive secretary of the General Advisory Committee for the AEC; returned to Los Alamos as assistant director for research.

Mark, J. Carson. (1913-1997) Canadian mathematician; part of British mission to the Manhattan Project in 1945, leader of T Division 1947-1973; oversaw development of hydrogen bomb in 1950s.

McCarthy, Senator Joseph. (1908-1957) Republican senator from Wisconsin, elected in 1946; launched investigations and made charges of subversive activity, censured by Senate for behavior "contrary to senatorial traditions."

McKee, Robert E. (1899-1964) Among most important contractors in US; built naval docks and Marine hospital at San Diego naval base, power plant at Pearl Harbor; chosen to be responsible for building facilities in Los Alamos; later became major contractor for the airport at Los Angeles (LAX).

McMahon, Senator Brien. (1903-1952) Democratic senator from Connecticut; responsible for Atomic Energy Act of 1946; became chairman of Joint Committee for Atomic Energy in 1948.

McNamara, Robert. (b. 1916) Secretary of Defense under Presidents Kennedy and Johnson, 1961-1968.

Murray, Arthur. (1914-2001) Worked in H Division making labeled compounds for use in research hospitals.

Oakes, Dr. William. (1913-1987) Came to Los Alamos in 1947 as chief of surgery at local hospital and consultant to the Laboratory on medical problems related to radiation exposure; physician in the Laboratory's Health Division from 1974 to 1981.

Oppenheimer, J. Robert. (1904-1967) Scientific director of Project Y, "father of the atomic bomb."

Parsons, Captain William D. (1901-1953) Known as Deke, Deac, or Deak (for Deacon); came to Los Alamos from Naval Proving Ground, Dahlgren, VA, as Groves's choice for ordnance chief and assistant director; bomb commander of Hiroshima mission on Enola Gay.

Petrzhak, Konstantin Antonovich. (1907-1998) One of Russian founders of nuclear physics research; work with Flerov led to discovery of spontaneous fission of atomic nuclei.

Rabi, I. I. (1898-1988) Austrian-born physicist; associate director at MIT, worked on development of radar; served as frequent consultant to Project Y.

Rickover, Admiral Hyman. (1900-1986) "Father of the nuclear navy"; planned and directed constructon of the submarine Nautilus, first atomic-powered submarine.

Rosen, Louis. (b. 1918) Joined Project Y in 1944; leader in development of world's most powerful linear accelerator; led to construction of LAMPF, now LANSCE; director of that facility until 1986; Senior Fellow Emeritus of LANL; recipient of LANL's most prestigious award, the Los Alamos Medal.

Rosenbluth, Marshall. (1927-2003) Worked in Los Alamos from 1950 until 1956; one of Edward Teller's principal theoreticians.

Roy, Max. (1910-1992) Leader of X Division immediately after WW II.

Schreiber, Raemer. (1910-1998) Joined Manhattan Project in 1943; part of pit assembly team for Trinity test; helped assemble the Nagasaki bomb; led pit assembly in Operation Crossroads; became division leader of W Division in 1951, leader of N Division's Rover project; deputy director of LANL from 1972 until his retirement in 1974.

Seaborg, Glenn T. (1912-1999) Directed nuclear chemical research and was associate director at Lawrence Radiation Laboratory; appointed by President Truman to first General Advisory Committee to the AEC; appointed to AEC by President Kennedy, 1962-1968.

Seeman, Colonel Lyle E. Army engineer, post commander; head of housing in early Los Alamos; assistant director for administration.

Shaw, Milt. (b. 1915) Member of AEC in 1969; naval protege of Admiral Rickover; focused on Liquid Metal Fast Breeder Reactor.

Spence, Rod. (b. 1913) Co-discoverer of fermium and einsteinium from debris left after the explosion of Mike; leader of radiochemistry research.

Sproul, Dr. Robert Gordon. (b. 1891) Eleventh president of University of California 1930-1958.

Strauss, Lewis L. (1896-1974) Appointed by President Truman to AEC in 1946, chairman 1953-58; strongly in favor of the hydrogen bomb; much opposed to Oppenheimer.

Teller, Edward. (1908-2005) Hungarian-born physicist; worked in T Division in Los Alamos; with Stan Ulam designed the hydrogen bomb.

Truman, Harry S. (1884-1972) US President 1945-1953; oversaw organization of the AEC.

Tuck, James. (1910-1980) Came to Los Alamos as part of the British delegation; helped develop the idea of explosive lensing for the implosion mechanism for the first atomic bomb; later was a leader in Project Sherwood.

Tyler, Carroll L. Manager of Santa Fe Area of the AEC; officer in charge in Los Alamos during which time the bridge over Los Alamos Canoyn was built; AEC's commanding official for the Ranger tests in Nevada in 1951.

Tyler, Colonel G. R. Commander in the Corps of Engineers in Los Alamos in 1945.

Ulam, Stanislaw. (1909-1984) Polish-born mathematician, physicist; solved the problem of how to initiate fusion in the hydrogen bomb; co-designer of the hydrogen bomb.

Underhill, Robert. Secretary of Board of Regents of the University of California; responsible for contract to operate Laboratory in Los Alamos.

von Neumann, John. (1903-1957) Hungarian-born mathematician; pioneer in computer science; worked in Theoretical Division in Manhattan Project.

Warner, Edith. (1891-1951) Lived in the house at Otowi Bridge; operated tearoom where many Laboratory scientists and their families enjoyed dining.

Wilhoyt, Colonel Ellis E. Head of Z-Division Office handling ordnance issues; Z-Division was moved to Sandia National Laboratory shortly after the war.

Glossary of Terms

AEC—Atomic Energy Commission, established by Congress in August 1946, became operative January 1, 1947. Its function was to oversee US nuclear activities; replaced in 1975 by the Energy Research and Development Administration (ERDA), and in 1977 by the Department of Energy (DOE).

Bikini—one of 29 atolls and 5 single islands that form the Republic of the Marshall Islands in the central Pacific; location of a series of nuclear tests in the 1940s and 1950s.

DAHRT—Dual Axis Radiographic Hydrodynamic Test facility consisting of two giant x-ray machines strong enough to see through metals; to analyze effects of implosions in mock-up experiments, making actual weapons testing unnecessary.

DOD—Department of Defense.

DOE—Department of Energy; see AEC.

Eniwetok (also Enewetak, Enewetok)—a small circular atoll in the central Pacific surrounding a large lagoon; the site of atomic tests from 1947 until 1962.

Fat Man—atomic bomb tested at Trinity Site July 16, 1945, and dropped on Nagasaki, Japan, August 9, 1945.

GAC—General Advisory Committee to the Atomic Energy Commission.

Gadget—the name suggested by Oppenheimer to replace the word *bomb* in the Manhattan Project.

Gnome—1961 underground nuclear test developed by Lawrence Livermore National Laboratory; first test in the Plowshare Program, designed to discover peaceful uses of nuclear energy. Its location is near the present site in southern New Mexico of the Waste Isolation Pilot Plant.

Greenhouse—four atmospheric tests at Eniwetok in 1951; two of the four, Dog and Easy, were tests of the Mark 6 (based on Fat Man) and the Mark 5 before they entered production. George was a thermonuclear experiment in the series.

HE—high explosives.

Honest John—first nuclear-tipped rocket, developed in 1953.

LAHS—Los Alamos Historical Society.

LAMPF—Los Alamos Meson Physics Facility, later LANSCE.

LAMPRE—Los Alamos Molten Plutonium Reactor Experiment.

LANL—Los Alamos National Laboratory; originally called Los Alamos Atomic Bomb Laboratory, growing into Los Alamos Laboratory and by 1947 becoming Los Alamos Scientific Laboratory. Since 1981 it has been Los Alamos National Laboratory.

LANSCE—Los Alamos Nuclear Science Conference, formerly LAMPF.

Little Boy—first atomic bomb used in warfare, detonated on August 6, 1945, over Hiroshima, Japan. Because of a shortage of uranium, as well as a surer probability of success for Little Boy, Fat Man was the device tested at Trinity Site July 16, 1945.

LNTBT—Limited Nuclear Test Ban Treaty entered into in 1963 by the US, UK, and USSR; the precursor to the Non-Proliferation Treaty of 1968.

MANIAC—Mathematical Numerical Integrator and Computer, giant computer designed and built by the Theoretical Division at LASL in 1952.

Mike—first hydrogen bomb detonation; thermonuclear device that obliterated an island in the Eniwetok Atoll, leaving a 164-foot deep crater where the island had been; not a usable weapon but it proved that thermonuclear fusion was possible.

NTS—Nevada Test Site, near Las Vegas, where nuclear testing occurred from 1951 until 1963.

Operation Crossroads—first post-World War II nuclear tests, held on the Bikini Atoll in the Marshall Islands. Two tests, Able and Baker, were designed to assess the effects of atomic detonations on naval ships. Able, a high altitude drop, missed its exact target and sank only five ships; Baker was a shallow-water detonation that sank only eight ships, but it irradiated the sea water washing over the entire fleet, rendering all the ships uninhabitable.

PHERMEX—Pulsed High-Energy Radiation Machine Emitting X-rays; for high explosives testing, diagnostic capability to study behavior of nuclear weapons; phased out by DARHT.

Project Plowshare—initial attempt to turn nuclear energy into peaceful, non-weapon applications.

Ranger—five air-dropped detonations in the winter of 1951; first tests at the Nevada Test Site, and first in the US proper since Trinity in 1945.

Rover—joint effort by LANL and the Air Force begun in 1955 to develop technology for nuclear rocket propulsion capable of sending large rockets beyond Mars or outside the solar system.

Sandstone—second test series in the Marshall Islands, 1948, designed to test improved design of nuclear weapons.

Scylla—developed to control thermonuclear power; first to produce true nuclear fusion in a laboratory.

Sherwood—national program to achieve magnetic fusion energy.

STRETCH—IBM's first attempt to build a super computer, the 7030 delivered to Los Alamos in 1961; fastest in the world until 1964.

"Super"—name assigned to the hydrogen bomb, thermonuclear device.

Trinity—name given to the explosion of the first atomic bomb, July 16, 1945, near Alamogordo, New Mexico.

UHTREX—Ultra High-Temperature Reactor Experiment.

Vela—satellites deployed in pairs to detect nuclear explosions in the atmosphere.

The Los Alamos Story

Monographs

1. *Los Alamos, New Mexico a survey to 1949.*
   Marjorie Bell Chambers and Linda K. Aldrich,
   1999.

2. *Robert Oppenheimer 1904-1967.*
   Robert F. Bacher, 1999.

3. *The Battle for Civil Rights or How Los Alamos
   Became a County.*
   Marjorie Bell Chambers, 1999.

4. *Quads, Shoeboxes and Sunken Living Rooms
   A History of Los Alamos Housing.*
   Craig Martin, 2000.

5. *Norris Bradbury 1909-1997.*
   Virginia Nylander Ebinger, editor, 2006.

Los Alamos Historical Society
Los Alamos, New Mexico